PENGUIN BOOKS

War

Roald Dahl is best known for his mischievous, wildly inventive stories for children. But throughout his life he was also a prolific and acclaimed writer of stories for adults. These sinister, surprising tales continue to entertain, amuse and shock generations of readers even today.

War

ROALD DAHL

PENGUIN BOOKS

PENGUIN BOOKS

UK | USA | Canada | Ireland | Australia
India | New Zealand | South Africa

Penguin Books is part of the Penguin Random House group of companies
whose addresses can be found at global.penguinrandomhouse.com.

These stories have been previously published in a variety of publications.
Details of each story's original publication are provided at the start of each
chapter and constitute an extension of this copyright page.
This collection first published in Penguin Books 2017

001

Set in 12.5/14.75 pt GaramondMTStd
Typeset by Jouve (UK), Milton Keynes
Printed in Great Britain by Clays Ltd, St Ives plc

A CIP catalogue record for this book is available from the British Library

ISBN: 978–1–405–93501–2

www.greenpenguin.co.uk

Contents

Haifa, June 1941

Going Solo

First published by Jonathan Cape Ltd (1986)

For Sofie Magdalene Dahl, 1885–1967

A life is made up of a great number of small incidents and a small number of great ones. An autobiography must therefore, unless it is to become tedious, be extremely selective, discarding all the inconsequential incidents in one's life and concentrating upon those that have remained vivid in the memory.

The first part of this book takes up my own personal story precisely where my earlier autobiography, which was called *Boy*, left off. I am away to East Africa on my first job, but because any job, even if it is in Africa, is not continuously enthralling, I have tried to be as selective as possible and have written only about those moments that I consider memorable.

In the second part of the book, which deals with the time I went flying with the RAF in the Second World War, there was no need to select or discard because every moment was, to me at any rate, totally enthralling.

R.D.

East Africa

The Voyage Out

The ship that was carrying me away from England to Africa in the autumn of 1938 was called the SS *Mantola*. She was an old paint-peeling tub of 9,000 tons with a single tall funnel and a vibrating engine that rattled the tea-cups in their saucers on the dining-room table.

The voyage from the Port of London to Mombasa would take two weeks and on the way we were going to call in at Marseilles, Malta, Port Said, Suez, Port Sudan and Aden. Nowadays you can fly to Mombasa in a few hours and you stop nowhere and nothing is fabulous any more, but in 1938 a journey like that was full of stepping-stones and East Africa was a long way from home, especially if your contract with the Shell Company said that you were to stay out there for three years at a stretch. I was twenty-two when I left. I would be twenty-five before I saw my family again.

What I still remember so clearly about that voyage is the extraordinary behaviour of my fellow passengers. I had never before encountered that peculiar Empire-building breed of Englishman who spends his whole life working in distant corners of British territory. Please do not forget that in the 1930s the British Empire was still very much the British Empire, and the men and women who kept it going were a race of people that most of you have never encountered and now you never will. I

S.S. "Mantola"
Saturday morning.

Dear Leonie

We've had a marvellous journey
Being calm in the Bay of Biscay (at least I
wasn't sick.) Then as soon as we came
to the Spanish coast the sun came out,
and it has stayed out ever since. We
passed Gibraltar Wednesday morning...

consider myself very lucky to have caught a glimpse of this rare species while it still roamed the forests and foot-hills of the earth, for today it is totally extinct. More English than the English, more Scottish than the Scots, they were the craziest bunch of humans I shall ever meet. For one thing, they spoke a language of their own. If they worked in East Africa, their sentences were sprinkled with Swahili words, and if they lived in India then all manner of dialects were intermingled. As well as this, there was a whole vocabulary of much-used words that seemed to be universal among all these people. An even-ing drink, for example, was always a sundowner. A drink at any other time was a chota peg. One's wife was the memsahib. To have a look at something was to have a shufti. And from that one, interestingly enough, RAF/Middle East slang for a reconnaissance plane in the last war was a shufti kite. Something of poor quality was shenzi. Supper was tiffin and so on and so forth. The Empire-builders' jargon would have filled a dictionary. All in all, it was rather wonderful for me, a conventional young lad from the suburbs, to be thrust suddenly into the middle of this pack of sinewy sunburnt gophers and their bright bony little wives, and what I liked best of all about them was their eccentricities.

It would seem that when the British live for years in a foul and sweaty climate among foreign people they main-tain their sanity by allowing themselves to go slightly dotty. They cultivate bizarre habits that would never be tolerated back home, whereas in far-away Africa or in Ceylon or in India or in the Federated Malay States they could do as they liked. On the SS *Mantola* just about every-body had his or her own particular maggot in the brain, and for me it was like watching a kind of non-stop panto-mime throughout the entire voyage. Let me tell you about two or three of these comedians.

I was sharing my cabin with the manager of a cotton mill in the Punjab called U. N. Savory (I could hardly believe those initials when I first saw them on his trunk) and I had the upper berth. From my pillow I could there-fore look out of the port-hole clear across the lifeboat deck and over the wide blue ocean beyond. On our fourth morning at sea I happened to wake up very early. I lay in my bunk gazing idly through the port-hole and listening to the gentle snores of U. N. Savory, who lay immediately below me. Suddenly, the figure of a naked man, naked as a jungle ape, went swooshing past the port-hole and dis-appeared! He had come and gone in absolute silence and I lay there wondering whether perhaps I had seen a phan-tom or a vision or even a naked ghost.

A minute or two later the naked figure went by again!

This time I sat up sharply. I wanted to get a better look at this leafless phantom of the sunrise, so I crawled down to the foot of my bunk and stuck my head through the port-hole. The lifeboat deck was deserted. The Mediterra-nean was calm and milky blue and a brilliant yellow sun was just edging up over the horizon. The deck was so empty and silent that I began to wonder seriously whether I might not after all have seen a genuine apparition, the ghost perhaps of a passenger who had fallen overboard on an earlier voyage and who now spent his eternal life running above the waves and clambering back on to his lost ship.

All of a sudden, from my little spy-hole, I spotted a movement at the far end of the deck. Then a naked body materialized. But this was no ghost. It was all too solid flesh, and the man was moving swiftly over the deck between the lifeboats and the ventilators and making no sound at all as he came galloping towards me. He was short and stocky and slightly pot-bellied in his nakedness, with a big black moustache on his face, and when he was twenty yards away he caught sight of my silly head sticking out of the port-hole and he waved a hairy arm at me and called out, 'Come along, my boy! Come and join me in a canter! Blow some sea air into your lungs! Get yourself in trim! Shake off the flab!'

By his moustache alone I recognized him as Major Griffiths, a man who had told me only the night before at the dinner table how he had spent thirty-six years in India and was returning once again to Allahabad after the usual home leave.

I smiled weakly at the Major as he went prancing by, but I didn't pull back. I wanted to see him again. There was something rather admirable about the way he was galloping round and round the deck with no clothes on at all, something wonderfully innocent and unembarrassed and cheerful and friendly. And here was I, a bundle of youthful self-consciousness, gaping at him through the port-hole and disapproving quite strongly of what he was doing. But I was also envying him. I was actually jealous of his total don't-give-a-damn attitude, and I wished like mad that I myself had the guts to go out there and do the same thing. I wanted to be like him. I longed to be able to fling off my pyjamas and go scampering round the deck in the altogether and to hell with anyone who happened to see me. But not in a million years could I have done it. I waited for him to come round again.

Ah, there he was! I could see him far away down the deck, the gallant galloping Major who didn't give a fig for anybody, and I decided right then that I would say something very casual to him this time to show him I was 'one of the gang' and that I had not even noticed his nakedness.

But hang on a minute! . . . What was this? . . . There was someone with him! . . . There was another fellow scooting along beside him this time! . . . As naked as the Major he was, too! . . . What on earth was going on aboard this ship? . . . Did *all* the male passengers get up at dawn and go tearing round the deck with no clothes on? . . . Was this some Empire-building body-building ritual I didn't know about? . . . The two were coming closer now . . . My God, the second one looked like a woman! . . . It *was* a woman! . . . A naked woman as bare-bosomed as Venus de Milo . . . But there the resemblance ceased for I could see now that this scrawny white-skinned figure was none other than Mrs Major Griffiths herself . . . I froze in my port-hole and my eyes became riveted on this nude female scarecrow galloping ever so proudly alongside her bare-skinned spouse, her elbows bent and her head held high, as much as to say, 'Aren't we a jolly fine couple, the two of us, and isn't he a fine figure of a man, my husband the Major?'

'Come along there!' the Major called out to me. 'If the little memsahib can do it, so can you! Fifty times round the deck is only four miles!'

'Lovely morning,' I murmured as they went galloping by. 'Beautiful day.'

A couple of hours later, I was sitting opposite the Major and his little memsahib at breakfast in the dining-room, and the knowledge that not long ago I had seen that same little memsahib with not a stitch on her made my spine creep. I kept my head down and pretended neither of them were there.

'Ha!' the Major cried suddenly. 'Aren't you the young fellow who had his head sticking through the port-hole this morning?'

'Who, me?' I murmured, keeping my nose in the cornflakes.

'Yes, you!' the Major cried, triumphant. 'I never forget a face!'

'I . . . I was just getting a breath of air,' I mumbled.

'You were getting a darn sight more than that!' the Major cried out, grinning. 'You were getting an eyeful of the memsahib, that's what you were doing!'

The whole of our table of eight people suddenly became silent and looked in my direction. I felt my cheeks beginning to boil.

'I can't say I blame you,' the Major went on, giving his wife an enormous wink. It was his turn to be proud and gallant now. 'In fact, I don't blame you at all. Would *you* blame him?' he asked, addressing the rest of the table. 'After all, we're only young once. And, as the poet says . . .'

he paused, giving the dreadful wife another colossal wink . . . 'a thing of beauty is a joy for ever.'

'Oh, do shut up, Bonzo,' the wife said, loving it.

'Back in Allahabad,' the Major said, looking at *me* now, 'I make a point of playing half-a-dozen chukkas every morning before breakfast. Can't do that on board ship, you know. So I have to get my exercise in other ways.'

I sat there wondering how one played this game of chuckers. 'Why can't you do it?' I said, desperate to change the subject.

'Why can't I do what?' the Major said.

'Play chuckers on the ship?' I said.

The Major was one of those men who chewed his porridge. He stared at me with pale-grey glassy eyes, chewing slowly. 'I hope you're not trying to tell me that you have never played polo in your life,' he said.

'Polo,' I said. 'Ah yes, of course, polo. At school we used to play it on bicycles with hockey sticks.'

The Major's stare switched suddenly to a fierce glare and he stopped chewing. He glared at me with such contempt and horror, and his face went so crimson, I thought he might be going to have a seizure.

From then on, neither the Major nor his wife would have anything to do with me. They changed their table in the dining-room and they cut me dead whenever we met on deck. I had been found guilty of a great and unforgivable crime. I had jeered, or so they thought, at the game of polo, the sacred sport of Anglo-Indians and royalty. Only a bounder would do that.

Then there was the elderly Miss Trefusis, who quite

often sat at the same dining-room table as me. Miss Trefusis was all bones and grey skin, and when she walked her body was bent forward in a long curve like a boomerang. She told me she owned a small coffee farm in the highlands of Kenya and that she had known Baroness Blixen very well. I myself had read and loved both *Out of Africa* and *Seven Gothic Tales*, and I listened enthralled to everything Miss Trefusis told me about that fine writer who called herself Isak Dinesen.

'She was dotty, of course,' Miss Trefusis said. 'Like all of us who live out there, she went completely dotty in the end.'

'*You* aren't dotty,' I said.

'Oh yes, I am,' she said firmly and very seriously. 'Everyone on this ship is as dotty as a dumpling. *You* don't notice it because you're young. Young people are not watchful. They only look at themselves.'

'I saw Major Griffiths and his wife running round the deck naked the other morning,' I said.

'You call that dotty?' Miss Trefusis said with a snort. 'That's *normal*.'

'*I* didn't think so.'

'You've got a few shocks coming to you, young man, before you're very much older, you mark my words,' she said. 'People go quite barmy when they live too long in Africa. That's where you're off to, isn't it?'

'Yes,' I said.

'You'll go barmy for sure,' she said, 'like the rest of us.'

She was eating an orange at the time and I noticed suddenly that she was not eating it in the normal way. In the first place she had speared it from the fruit bowl with her fork instead of taking it in her fingers. And now, with knife and fork, she was making a series of neat incisions in the skin all around the orange. Then, very delicately, using the points of her knife and fork, she peeled the skin away in eight separate pieces, leaving the bare fruit beautifully exposed. Still using knife and fork, she separated the juicy segments and began to eat them slowly, one by one, with her fork.

'Do you always eat an orange like that?' I said.

'Of course.'

'May I ask why?'

'I never touch anything I eat with my fingers,' she said.

'Good Lord, don't you really?'

'Never. I haven't since I was twenty-two.'

'Is there a reason for that?' I asked her.

'Of course there's a reason. Fingers are filthy.'

'But you wash your hands.'

'I don't *sterilize* them,' Miss Trefusis said. 'Nor do you. They're full of bugs. Disgusting dirty things, fingers. Just think what you do with them!'

I sat there going through the things I did with my fingers.

'It doesn't bear thinking about, does it?' Miss Trefusis said. 'Fingers are just implements. They are the gardening implements of the body, the shovels and the forks. You push them into everything.'

'We seem to survive,' I said.

'Not for long you won't,' she said darkly.

I watched her eating her orange, spearing the little

boats one after the other with her fork. I could have told her that the fork wasn't sterilized either, but I kept quiet.

'Toes are even worse,' she said suddenly.

'I beg your pardon?'

'They're the worst of all,' she said.

'What's wrong with toes?'

'They are the nastiest part of the human body!' she announced vehemently.

'Worse than fingers?'

'There's no comparison,' she snapped. 'Fingers are foul and filthy, but *toes*! *Toes* are reptilian and viperish! I don't wish to talk about them!'

I was getting a bit confused. 'But one doesn't eat with one's toes,' I said.

'I never said you did,' Miss Trefusis snapped.

'Then what's so awful about them?' I persisted.

'Uck!' she said. 'They are like little worms sticking out of your feet. I hate them, I hate them! I can't bear to look at them!'

'Then how do you cut your toenails?'

'I don't,' she said. 'My boy does it for me.'

I wondered why she was 'Miss' if she'd been married and had a boy of her own. Perhaps he was illegitimate.

'How old is your son?' I asked, treading carefully.

'No, no, no!' she cried. 'Don't you know *anything*? A "boy" is one's native servant. Didn't you learn that when you read Isak Dinesen?'

'Ah yes, of course,' I said, remembering.

Absent-mindedly I took an orange myself and was about to start peeling it.

'Don't,' Miss Trefusis said, shuddering. 'You'll catch something if you do that. Use your knife and fork. Go on. Try it.'

I tried it. It was rather fun. There was something satisfying about cutting the skin to just the right depth and then peeling away the segments.

'There you are,' she said. 'Well done.'

'Do you employ a lot of "boys" on your coffee farm?' I asked her.

'About fifty,' she said.

'Do they go barefoot?'

'Mine don't,' she said. 'No one works for me without shoes on. It costs me a fortune, but it's worth it.'

I liked Miss Trefusis. She was impatient, intelligent, generous and interesting. I felt she would come to my rescue at any time, whereas Major Griffiths was vapid, vulgar, arrogant and unkind, the sort of man who'd leave you to the crocodiles. He might even push you in. Both of them, of course, were completely dotty. Everyone on the ship was dotty, but none, as it turned out, was quite as dotty as my cabin companion, U. N. Savory.

The first sign of *his* dottiness was revealed to me one evening as our ship was running between Malta and Port Said. It had been a stifling hot afternoon and I was having a brief rest on my upper berth before dressing for dinner.

Dressing? Oh yes, indeed. We all dressed for dinner every single evening on board that ship. The male species of the Empire-builder, whether he is camping in the jungle or is at sea in a rowing-boat, *always* dresses for dinner, and by that I mean white shirt, black tie, dinner-jacket, black trousers and black patent-leather shoes, the full regalia, and to hell with the climate.

I lay still on my bunk with my eyes half open. Below me, U. N. Savory was getting dressed. There wasn't room in the cabin for two of us to change our clothes simultaneously, so we took it in turns to go first. It was his turn to dress first tonight. He had tied his bow-tie and now he was putting on his black dinner-jacket. I was watching him rather dreamily through half-closed eyes, and I saw him reaching into his sponge-bag and take out a small carton. He stationed himself in front of the washbasin mirror, took the lid off the carton and dipped his fingers into it. The fingers came out with a pinch of white powder or crystals, and this stuff he proceeded to sprinkle very carefully over the shoulders of his dinner-jacket. Then he replaced the lid on the carton and put it back in the sponge-bag.

Suddenly I was fully alert. What on earth was the man up to? I didn't want him to know I'd seen, so I closed my eyes and pretended to be asleep. This is a rum business, I thought. Why in the world would U. N. Savory want to sprinkle white stuff on to the shoulders of his dinner-jacket? And what *was* it, anyway? Could it be some subtle perfume or a magic aphrodisiac? I waited until he had left the cabin, then, feeling only slightly guilty, I hopped down from my bunk and opened his sponge-bag. EPSOM SALTS, it said on the little carton! And Epsom salts it was! Now what good could Epsom salts possibly do him sprinkled on his shoulders? I had always thought of him as a queer fish, a man with secrets, though I hadn't discovered what they were. Under his bunk he kept a tin trunk and a black leather case. There was nothing odd about the tin trunk, but the case puzzled me. It was roughly the size of a violin case but the lid didn't bulge as the lid of a violin case does, and it wasn't tapered. It was simply a three-foot-long rectangular leather box with two very strong brass locks on it.

'Do you play the violin?' I had once said to him.

'Don't be daft,' he had answered. 'I don't even play the gramophone.'

Perhaps it contained a sawn-off shotgun then, I told myself. It was about the right size.

I put the carton of Epsom salts back in his sponge-bag, then I took a shower, dressed and went upstairs to have a drink before dinner. There was one stool vacant at the bar so I sat down and ordered a glass of beer. There were eight sinewy sunburnt gophers including U. N. Savory sitting on high stools at the bar. The stools were screwed to the floor. The bar was semi-circular so that everyone could talk across to everyone else. U. N. Savory was sitting about five places away from me. He was drinking a gimlet, which was the Empire-builder's name for a gin with lime juice in it. I sat there listening to the small talk about pig-sticking and polo and how curry will cure constipation. I felt a total outsider. There was nothing I could contribute to the conversation so I stopped listening and concentrated on trying to solve the riddle of the Epsom salts. I glanced at U. N. Savory. From where I sat, I could actually see the tiny white crystals on his shoulders.

Then a funny thing happened.

U. N. Savory suddenly began brushing the Epsom salts off one of his shoulders with his hand. He did it ostentatiously, slapping the shoulder quite hard and saying at the same time in a rather loud voice, 'Ruddy dandruff! I'm fed up with it! Do any of you fellers know a good cure?'

'Try coconut oil,' one said.

'Bay rum and cantharides,' another said.

A tea-planter from Assam called Unsworth said, 'Take my word for it, old man, you've got to stimulate the circulation in the scalp. And the way to do that is to dunk your hair in ice-cold water every morning and keep it there for five minutes. Then dry vigorously. You've got a fine head of hair at the moment, but you'll be as bald as a coot in no time if you don't cure that dandruff. You do as I say, old man.'

U. N. Savory did indeed have a fine head of black hair, so why in the world should he have wanted to pretend he had dandruff when he hadn't?

'Thanks a lot, old man,' U. N. Savory said. 'I'll give it a go. See if it works.'

'It'll work,' Unsworth told him. 'My grandmother cured her dandruff that way.'

'Your *grandmother*?' someone said. 'Did *she* have dandruff?'

'When she combed her hair', Unsworth said, 'it looked like it was snowing.'

For the hundredth time, I told myself that they were all totally and incurably dotty, every one of them, but I was beginning to think now that U. N. Savory might beat them all to it. I sat there staring into my beer and trying to figure out why he should go around trying to kid everyone he had dandruff. Three days later I had the answer.

It was early evening. We were moving slowly through the Suez Canal and it was hotter than ever. It was my turn to dress first for dinner. While I showered and put on my clothes, U. N. Savory lay on his bunk staring into space. 'It's all yours,' I said at last as I opened the door and went out. 'See you upstairs.'

As usual, I seated myself at the bar and began sipping a beer. By gosh, it was hot. The big slowly-revolving fan in the ceiling seemed to be blowing *steam* out of its blades. Sweat trickled down my neck and under my stiff butterfly collar. I could feel the starch in the collar going soggy around the back. The sinewy sunburnt ones around me didn't seem to notice the heat. I decided to go out on deck and smoke a pipe before dinner. It would be cooler there. I felt for my pipe. Damnation, I had left it behind. I stood up and made my way downstairs to the cabin and opened the door. There was a strange man sitting in shirtsleeves on U. N. Savory's bunk and as I stepped inside, the man gave a queer little yelp and jumped to his feet as though a cracker had gone off in the seat of his pants.

The stranger was totally bald and that is why it took me a second or two to realize that he was in fact none other than U. N. Savory himself. It is extraordinary how hair on the head or the lack of it will completely change a person's appearance. U. N. Savory looked like a different man. To start with, he looked fifteen years older, and in some subtle way he seemed also to have diminished, grown much

Suez Canal, near Ismailia

shorter and smaller. As I said, he was almost totally bald, and the dome of his head was as pink and shiny as a ripe peach. He was standing up now and holding in his two hands the wig he had been about to put on as I walked in. 'You had no right to come back!' he shouted. 'You said you'd finished!' Little sparks of fury were flashing in his eyes.

'I'm . . . I'm most awfully sorry,' I stammered. 'I forgot my pipe.'

He stood there glaring at me with that dark malevolent glint in his eye and I could see little droplets of perspiration oozing out of the pores on his bald head. I felt very bad. I didn't know what to say next. 'Just let me get my pipe and I'll clear out,' I mumbled.

'Oh no you don't!' he shouted. 'You've seen it now and you're not leaving this room until you've made me a promise! You've got to promise me you won't tell a soul! Promise me that!'

Behind him I could see that curious black leather 'violin case' lying open on his bunk, and in it, nestling alongside each other like three large black hairy hedgehogs, lay three more wigs.

'There's nothing wrong with being bald,' I said.

'I didn't ask for your opinion,' he shouted. He was still very angry. 'I just want your promise.'

'I won't tell anyone,' I said. 'I give you my word.'

'And you'd better keep it,' he said.

I reached out and took hold of the pipe that was lying on my bunk. Then I began rummaging round in various places for my tobacco pouch. U. N. Savory sat down on the lower bunk. 'I suppose you think I'm crazy,' he said. Suddenly all the bark had gone out of his voice.

I said nothing. I could think of nothing to say.

'You do, don't you?' he said. 'You think I'm crazy.'

'Not at all,' I answered. 'A man can do as he likes.'

'I'll bet you think it's just vanity,' he said. 'But it's not vanity. It's nothing to do with vanity.'

'It's OK,' I said. 'Really it is.'

'It's business,' he said. 'I do it purely for business reasons.

I work in Amritsar, in the Punjab. That is the homeland of the Sikhs. To a Sikh, hair is a sort of religion. A Sikh never cuts his hair. He either rolls it up on the top of his head or in a turban. A Sikh doesn't respect a bald man.'

'In that case I think it's very clever of you to wear a wig,' I said. I had to live in this cabin with U. N. Savory for several days yet and I didn't want a row. 'It's quite brilliant,' I added.

'Do you honestly think so?' he said, melting.

'It's a stroke of genius.'

'I go to a lot of trouble to convince all those Sikh wallahs it's my own hair,' he went on.

'You mean the dandruff bit?'

'You saw it, then?'

'Of course I saw it. It was brilliant.'

'It's just *one* of my little ruses,' he said. He was getting just a trifle smug now. 'No one's going to suspect me of wearing a wig if I've got dandruff, are they?'

'Certainly not. It's quite brilliant. But why bother doing it here? There aren't any Sikhs on this ship.'

'You never know,' he said darkly. 'You never can tell who might be lurking around the corner.'

The man was as potty as a pilchard.

'I see you have more than one,' I said, pointing to the black leather case.

'One's no good,' he said, 'not if you're going to do it properly like me. I always carry four, and they're all slightly different. You are forgetting that hair *grows*, old man, aren't you? Each one of these is longer than the other. I put on a longer one every week.'

'What happens after you've worn the longest one and you can't go any further?' I asked.

'Ah,' he said. 'That's the clincher.'

'I don't quite follow you.'

'I simply say, "Does anyone know of a good barber round here?" And the next day I start all over again with the shortest one.'

'But you said Sikhs didn't approve of cutting hair.'

'I only do that with Europeans,' he said.

I stared at him. The man was stark raving barmy. I felt I would go barmy myself if I went on talking to him much longer. I edged towards the door. 'I think you're amazing,' I said. 'You're quite brilliant. And don't worry about a thing. My lips are sealed.'

'Thanks old man,' U. N. Savory said. 'Good lad.'

I flew out of the cabin and shut the door.

And that is the story of U. N. Savory.

You don't believe it?

Listen, I could hardly believe it myself as I staggered upstairs to the bar.

I kept my promise, though. I told no one. Today it no longer matters. The man was at least thirty years older than me, so by now his soul is at rest and his wigs are probably being used by his nephews and nieces for playing charades.

SS Mantola
4 October 1938

Dear Mama,

We're now in the Red Sea, and it is hot. *The wind is behind us and going at exactly the same speed as the boat so there is not a breath of air on board. Three times they have turned the ship round against the wind to get some air into the cabins and into the engine room. Fans merely blow hot air into your face.*

The deck is strewn with a lot of limp wet things for all the world like a lot of wet towels steaming over the kitchen boiler. They just smoke cigarettes & shout, 'Boy – another iced lager.'

I don't feel the heat much – probably because I'm thin. In fact as soon as I've finished this letter I'm going off to have a vigorous game of deck tennis with another thin man – a government vet called Hammond. We play with our shirts off, throwing the coit as hard as we can –& when we have to stop for fear of drowning in our own sweat we just jump into the swimming bath.

Dar es Salaam

The temperature in the shade was around 120°F on board the SS *Mantola* as she crept southwards down the Red Sea towards Port Sudan. The breeze was behind us and it blew at exactly the same speed as the ship. There was, therefore, no movement of air at all on board. Three times during the first day they turned the ship around and sailed against the wind to blow some air through the port-holes and over the decks. This made little difference and even the sinewy sunburnt gophers and their tough bony little wives became silent and exhausted. Like me, they sprawled in deck-chairs under the awning, gasping for breath while the sweat ran down their faces and necks and arms and dripped from their elbows on to the wooden deck. It was even too hot to read.

During the second day in the Red Sea, the *Mantola* passed very close to an Italian ship which, like us, was going south. She wasn't more than 200 yards away from us and her decks were crowded with women! There must have been several thousand of them all over the ship and not a man in sight. I couldn't believe my eyes.

'What's going on?' I asked one of the ship's officers, who was standing near me on the rail. 'Why all the girls?'

'They're for the Italian soldiers,' he said.

'What Italian soldiers?'

'The ones in Abyssinia,' he said. 'Mussolini is trying to conquer Abyssinia and he's got a hundred thousand troops in there. Now they are shipping out Italian girls to keep the soldiers happy.'

'You're pulling my leg.'

'They're going out in boatloads,' the officer said. 'One girl for every soldier in the ranks, two for each Colonel and three for a General.'

'Be serious,' I said.

'They really *are* for the soldiers,' he said. 'It is such a rotten pointless war and the soldiers all hate it and they are fed up with massacring the wretched Abyssinians. So Mussolini is sending out thousands of girls to boost their morale.'

Crossing The Equator. Me being ducked.

I waved to the girls on the other ship and about 2,000 of them waved back at me. They seemed very cheerful. I wondered how long they would be feeling that way.

At last the *Mantola* reached Mombasa, and there I was met by a man from the Shell Company who told me I was to proceed at once down the coast to Dar es Salaam, in Tanganyika (now Tanzania). 'It will take you a day and a night to get there,' he said, 'and you travel on a little coastal vessel called the *Dumra*. Here's your ticket.'

I transferred to the *Dumra* and it sailed the same day. That evening we called in at Zanzibar where the air was filled with the amazing spicy-sweet scent of cloves, and I stood by the rail gazing at the old Arab town and thinking what a lucky young fellow I was to be seeing all these marvellous places free of charge and with a good job at the end of it all. We left Zanzibar at midnight and I went to bed in my tiny cabin knowing that tomorrow would be journey's end.

When I woke up the next morning the ship's engines had stopped. I jumped out of my bunk and peered through the port-hole. This was my first glimpse of Dar es Salaam and I have never forgotten it. We were anchored out in the middle of a vast rippling blue-black lagoon and all around the rim of the lagoon there were pale-yellow sandy beaches, almost white, and breakers were running up on to the sand, and coconut palms with their little green leafy hats were growing on the beaches, and there were casuarina trees, immensely tall and breathtakingly beautiful with their delicate grey-green foliage. And then behind the casuarinas was what seemed to me like a jungle, a great tangle of tremendous dark-green trees that were full of shadows and almost certainly teeming, so I told myself, with rhinos and lions and all manner of vicious beasts. Over to one side lay the tiny town of Dar es Salaam, the houses white and yellow and pink, and among the houses I could see a narrow church steeple and a domed mosque and along the waterfront there was a line of acacia trees splashed with scarlet flowers. A fleet of canoes was rowing out to take us ashore and the black-skinned rowers were chanting weird songs in time with their rowing.

The whole of that amazing tropical scene through the port-hole has been photographed on my mind ever since. To me it was all wonderful, beautiful and exciting. And so it remained for the rest of my time in Tanganyika. I loved

Dar-es-Salaam Harbour

it all. There were no furled umbrellas, no bowler hats, no sombre grey suits and I never once had to get on a train or a bus.

Only three young Englishmen ran the Shell Company in the whole of that vast territory, and I was the youngest

Shell House, Dar-es-Salaam

and the junior. When we were not 'on the road', we lived in the splendid large Shell Company house perched on the top of the cliffs outside Dar es Salaam, and we were treated like princes. Our domestic staff consisted of a male native cook affectionately called Piggy because the Swahili for cook is *mpishi*. There was a shamba-boy or gardener called Salimu and a personal 'boy' for each of us. Your boy was really a kind of valet and jack of all trades. He was expert at sewing and mending and washing and ironing and polishing and making sure there weren't scorpions in your mosquito boots before you put them on, and he became your friend. He looked after nobody else but you and there was nothing he did not know about your life and your habits. In return, you looked after him and his wives (never less than two) and his children who lived in their own quarters at the back of the house.

My boy was called Mdisho. He was a Mwanumwezi tribesman, which meant a lot out there because the Mwanumwezi was the only tribe who had ever defeated the gigantic Masai in battle. Mdisho was tall and graceful and soft-spoken, and his loyalty to me, his young white English master, was absolute. I hope, and I believe, that I was equally loyal to him.

The first thing you had to do when you came to work in Dar es Salaam was to learn Swahili, otherwise you could not communicate either with your own boy or with any other native of the country because none of them spoke a word of English. In those benighted days of Empire it was considered impertinent for a black man to understand English, let alone to speak it. The result was that none of them made any effort to learn our language, so we had to learn theirs instead. Swahili is a relatively simple language, and with the help of a Swahili–English dictionary and a grammar book, plus some hard work in the evenings, you could become pretty fluent in a couple of months. Then you took an exam and if you passed it, the Shell Company gave you a bonus of a hundred pounds, which was a lot of money in those days when a case of whisky cost only twelve pounds.

..., v. lazimu.

Conceal, v. ncha, setiri.
Concubine, s., suria, plur. ma-.
be Condemned, v. (by a judge) pasishwa hatia.
Condition, s. hali, (necessary requirement) kanuni.
Conduct, s. mwenendo, matendo, (good conduct) adili.
Conduct, v. peleka, leta, fikisha.
Confess, v. ungama.
Confidence, s. matumaini.
become Confident, v. tumaini.
come Confused, v. (of persons) ... (of things) chafuka.

ongea.
Convert, s. mwongofu.
Convert, v. ongoa, geuza.
be Converted, v. ongoka, geuka.
Cook, v. pika.
Cook, s. mpishi.
Cooked rice, s. wali.
Cooking-place, s. jiko.
Cooking-pot, s. (earthenware) chungu, mkungu, (metal) sufuria.
Cooking-stones, s. (to rest a pot on) mafya.
Cool, a. -a baridi.
Cool ...) poza.

my Swahili dictionary

Sometimes I would have to go on safari upcountry and Mdisho always came with me. We would take the Shell station-wagon and be gone for a month, driving all over Tanganyika on dirt roads that were covered with millions of tiny close-together ruts. Driving over those ruts in a station-wagon felt as though you were riding on top of a gigantic vibrator. We would drive far west to the edge of Lake Tanganyika in central Africa and on down south to the borders of Nyasaland, and after that we would head east towards Mozambique, and the purpose of these trips was to visit our Shell customers. These customers ran diamond mines and gold mines and sisal plantations and cotton plantations and goodness knows what else besides, and my job was to keep their machinery supplied with the proper grades of lubricating oil and fuel oil. Not a great deal of intelligence or imagination was required, but by gum you needed to be fit and tough.

I loved that life. We saw giraffe standing unafraid right beside the road nibbling the tops of the trees. We saw plenty of elephant and hippo and zebra and antelope and very occasionally a pride of lions. The only creatures I was frightened of were the snakes. We used often to see a big one gliding across the dirt road ahead of the car, and the golden rule was never to accelerate and try to run it over, especially if the roof of the car was open, as ours often was. If you hit a snake at speed, the front wheel can flip it up into the air and there is a danger of it landing in your lap. I can think of nothing worse than that.

The really bad snake in Tanganyika is the black mamba. It is the only one that has no fear of man and will deliberately attack him on sight. If it bites you, you are a gonner.

One morning I was shaving myself in the bathroom of our Dar es Salaam house, and as I lathered my face I was absent-mindedly gazing out of the window into the garden. I was watching Salimu, our shamba-boy, as he slowly and methodically raked the gravel on the front drive. Then I saw the snake. It was six feet long and thick as my arm and quite black. It was a mamba all right and there was no doubt that it had seen Salimu and was gliding fast over the gravel straight towards him.

I flung myself toward the open window and yelled in Swahili, 'Salimu! Salimu! Angalia nyoka kubwa! Nyuma wewe! Upesi upesi!', in other words, 'Salimu! Salimu! Beware huge snake! Behind you! Quickly quickly!'

The mamba was moving over the gravel at the speed of a running man and when Salimu turned and saw it, it could not have been more than fifteen paces away from him. There was nothing more I could do. There was not much Salimu could do either. He knew it was useless to run because a mamba at full speed could travel as fast as a galloping horse. And he certainly knew it was a mamba. Every native in Tanganyika knew what a mamba looked like and what to expect from it. It would reach him in another five seconds. I leant out of the window and held my breath. Salimu swung round and faced the snake. I saw him go into a crouch. He crouched very low with one leg behind the other like a runner about to start a hundred yard sprint, and he was holding the long rake out in front of him. He raised it, but no higher than his shoulder, and he stood there for those long four or five seconds absolutely motionless, watching the great black deadly snake as it glided so quickly over the gravel towards him. Its small triangular snake's head was raised up in the air, and I could hear the soft rustling of the gravel as the body slid over the loose stones. I have the whole nightmarish picture of that scene still before my eyes – the morning sunshine on the garden, the massive baobab tree in the background, Salimu in his old khaki shorts and shirt and bare feet standing brave and absolutely still with the upraised rake in his hands, and to one side the long black snake gliding over the gravel straight towards him with its small poisonous head held high and ready to strike.

Salimu waited. He never moved or made a sound during the time it took the snake to reach him. He waited until the very last moment when the mamba was not more than five feet away and then *wham*! Salimu struck first. He brought the metal prongs of the rake down hard right on to the middle of the mamba's back and he held the rake there with all his weight, leaning forward now and jumping up and down to put more weight on the fork in an effort to pin the snake to the ground. I saw the blood spurt where the prongs had gone right into the snake's body and then I rushed downstairs absolutely naked, grabbing a golf club as I went through the hall, and outside on the drive Salimu was still there pressing with both hands on the rake and the great snake was writhing and twisting and throwing itself about, and I shouted to Salimu in Swahili, 'What shall I do?'

'It is all right now, bwana!' he shouted back. 'I have broken its back and it cannot travel forward any more! Stand away, bwana! Stand well away and leave it to me!'

Salimu lifted the rake and jumped away and the snake went on writhing and twisting but it was quite unable to travel in any direction. The boy went forward and hit it accurately and very hard on the head with the metal end of the rake and suddenly the snake stopped moving. Salimu let out a great sigh and passed a hand over his forehead. Then he looked at me and smiled.

'Asanti, bwana,' he said, 'asanti sana,' which simply means, 'Thank you, bwana. Thank you very much.'

It isn't often one gets the chance to save a person's life. It gave me a good feeling for the rest of the day, and from then on, every time I saw Salimu, the good feeling would come back to me.

Dar es Salaam
19 March 1939

Dear Mama,
    If a war breaks out you've jolly well got to go to Tenby otherwise you'll be bombed. Don't forget, you've got to go if war breaks out . . .

Simba

About a month after the black mamba incident, I set out on a safari upcountry in the old Shell station-wagon with Mdisho and our first stop was the small town of Bagomoyo. I mention this only because the name of the Indian trader I had to go and see in Bagomoyo was so wonderful I have never been able to get it out of my mind. He was a tiny little man with an immense low-slung protuberant belly of the kind that women have when they are eight and a half months pregnant, and he carried this great ball in front of him very proudly, as if it were a special medal or a coat of arms. He called himself Mister Shankerbai Ganderbai, and across the top of his business notepaper was printed in red capital letters the full title he had conferred upon himself, MISTER SHANKERBAI GANDERBAI OF BAGOMOYO, SELLER OF DECORTICATORS. A decorticator is a huge clanking piece of machinery that converts the leaves of the sisal plant into fibres for making rope, and if you wanted to buy one, the man to go and see was Mister Shankerbai Ganderbai of Bagomoyo.

After three more days of dusty travelling and visiting customers, Mdisho and I came to the town of Tabora. Tabora is some 450 miles inland from Dar es Salaam, and in 1939 it was not much of a town, just a scattering of houses and a few streets where the Indian traders had their shops. But because by Tanganyikan standards it was a sizeable place, it was honoured by the presence of a British District Officer.

The District Officers in Tanganyika were a breed I admired. Admittedly they were sunburnt and sinewy, but they were not gophers. They were all university graduates with good degrees, and in their lonely outposts they had to be all things to all men. They were the judges whose decisions settled both tribal and personal disputes. They were the advisers to tribal chiefs. They were often the givers of medicines and the saviours of the sick. They administered their own vast districts by keeping law and order under the most difficult circumstances. And wherever there was a District Officer, the Shell man on safari was welcome to stay the night at his house.

The DO in Tabora was called Robert Sanford, a man in his early thirties who had a wife and three very small children, a boy of six, a girl of four and a baby.

That evening I was sitting on the veranda having a sundowner with Robert Sanford and his wife Mary, while two of the children were playing out on the grass in front of the house under the watchful eye of their black nurse. The heat of the day was becoming less intense as the sun went down, and the first whisky and soda was tasting good.

'So what's been going on in Dar?' Robert Sanford asked me. 'Anything exciting?'

I told him about the black mamba and Salimu. When I had finished, Mary Sanford said, 'That's the one thing I'm always frightened of in this country, those beastly snakes.'

'Damn lucky you happened to see it behind him,' Robert Sanford said. 'He was certain to have been killed.'

'We had a spitting cobra near our back door not long ago,' Mary Sanford said. 'Robert shot it.'

The Sanford house was on a hill outside the town. It was a white wooden two-storey building with a roof of green tiles. The eaves of the house projected far out beyond the walls to provide extra shade, and this gave the building a sort of Japanese pagoda appearance. The surrounding countryside was to me a very pleasant sight. It was a vast brown plain with many quite large knolls and hummocks dotted all over it, and although the plain itself was mostly burnt-up scrubland, the hills were covered with all sorts of huge jungle trees, and their dense foliage made little emerald-green dots all over the plain. On the burnt-up plain itself there grew nothing but those bare spiky thorn trees that you find all over East Africa, and there were about six huge vultures sitting quite motionless on every thorn tree in sight. The vultures were brown with curved orange beaks and orange feet, and they spent their whole lives sitting and watching and waiting for some animal to die so they could pick its bones.

'Do you like this sort of life?' I said to Robert Sanford.

'I love the freedom,' he said. 'I administer about two thousand square miles of territory and I can go where I want and do more or less exactly as I please. That part of it is marvellous. But I do miss the company of other white men. There aren't many even moderately intelligent Europeans in the town.'

We sat there watching the sun go down behind the flat

Government House, Dar-es-Salaam

Haircut in
Dar-es-Salaam

Sundowner at Shell House

brown plain that was covered with thorn trees, and we could see the sinister vultures waiting like feathered undertakers for death to come along and give them something to work on.

'Keep the children a bit closer to the house!' Mary Sanford called out to the nurse. 'Bring them closer, please!'

Robert Sanford said, 'My mother sent me out Beethoven's Third Symphony from England last week. HMV, two records, four sides in all, Toscanini conducting. I'm using a thorn needle instead of a steel one so as not to wear out the grooves. It seems to work.'

'Don't you find the records warp a lot out here?' I asked.

'I keep them lying flat with a pile of books on top of them,' he said. 'What I'm terrified of is dropping one and breaking it.'

The sun had gone down now and a lovely soft light was spreading over the landscape. I could see a group of zebra grazing among the thorn trees about half a mile away. Robert Sanford was also watching the zebras.

'I keep wondering,' he said, 'if it wouldn't be possible to catch a young zebra and break it in for riding, just like a horse. After all, they are only wild horses with stripes on.'

'Has anyone ever tried?' I asked.

'Not that I know,' he said. 'Mary's a good rider. What do you think, darling? How would you like to have a private zebra to ride on?'

'It might be fun,' she said. Even though she had a bit of a jaw, she was a handsome woman. I didn't mind the jaw. The shape of it gave her the look of a fighter.

'Perhaps we could cross one with a horse,' Robert Sanford said, 'and call it a zorse.'

'Or a hebra,' Mary Sanford said.

'Right,' her husband said, smiling.

'Shall we try it?' Mary Sanford said. 'It would be rather splendid to have a baby zorse or hebra. Oh darling, *shall* we try it?'

'The children could ride it,' he said. 'A black zorse with white stripes all over it.'

'Please can we play your Beethoven after supper?' I said.

'Absolutely,' Robert Sanford said. 'I'll put the gramophone out here on the veranda and then those tremendous chords can go booming out through the night over the plain. It's terrific. The only trouble is I have to wind the thing up twice for each side.'

'I'll wind it for you,' I said.

Suddenly, the voice of a man yelling in Swahili exploded into the quiet of the evening. It was my boy, Mdisho. 'Bwana! Bwana! Bwana!' he was yelling from somewhere behind the house. 'Simba, bwana! Simba! Simba!'

Simba is Swahili for lion. All three of us leapt to our feet, and the next moment Mdisho came tearing round the corner of the house yelling at us in Swahili, 'Come quick, bwana! Come quick! Come quick! A huge lion is eating the wife of the cook!'

That sounds pretty funny when you put it on paper back here in England, but to us, standing on a veranda in the middle of East Africa, it was not funny at all.

Robert Sanford flew into the house and came out again

in five seconds flat holding a powerful rifle and ramming a cartridge into the breech. 'Get those children indoors!' he shouted to his wife as he ran down off the veranda with me behind him.

Mdisho was dancing about and pointing towards the back of the house and yelling in Swahili, 'The lion has taken the wife of the cook and the lion is eating her and the cook is chasing the lion and trying to save his wife!'

The servants lived in a series of low whitewashed out-buildings at the back of the house, and as we came running round the corner we saw four or five house-boys leaping about and pointing and shrieking, 'Simba! Simba! Simba!' The boys were all clothed in spotless white cotton robes that looked like long night-shirts, and each had a fine scarlet tarboosh on his head. The tarboosh is a sort of top-hat without a brim, and there is often a black tassel on it. The women had come out of their huts as well and were standing in a separate group, silent, immobile and staring.

'Where is it?' Robert Sanford shouted, but he had no need to ask, for we very quickly spotted the massive sandy-coloured lion not more than eighty or ninety yards off and trotting away from the house. He had a fine bushy collar of fur around his neck, and in his jaws he was holding the wife of the cook. The lion had the woman by the waist so that her head and arms hung down on one side and her legs on the other, and I could see that she was wearing a red and white spotted dress. The lion, so startlingly close, was loping away from us in the calmest possible manner with a slow, long-striding, springy lope, and behind the lion, not more than the length of a tennis court behind, ran the cook himself in his white cotton robe and with his red hat on his head, running most bravely and waving his arms like a whirlwind, leaping, clapping his hands, screaming, shouting, shouting, shouting, 'Simba! Simba! Simba! Simba! Let go of my wife! Let go of my wife!'

Oh, it was a scene of great tragedy and comedy both mixed up together, and now Robert Sanford was running full speed after the cook who was running after the lion. He was holding his rifle in both hands and shouting to the cook, 'Pingo! Pingo! Get out of the way, Pingo! Lie down on the ground so I can shoot the simba! You are in my way! You are *in my way*, Pingo!'

But the cook ignored him and kept on running, and the lion ignored everybody, not altering his pace at all but continuing to lope along with slow springy strides and with the head held high and carrying the woman proudly in his jaws, rather like a dog who is trotting off with a good bone.

Both the cook and Robert Sanford were travelling faster than the lion who really didn't seem to care about his pursuers at all. And as for me, I didn't know what to do to help them so I ran after Robert Sanford. It was an awkward situation because there was no way that Robert Sanford could take a shot at the lion without risking a hit on the cook's wife, let alone on the cook himself who was still right in his line of fire.

The lion was heading for one of those hillocks that was densely covered with jungle trees and we all knew that once he got in there, we would never be able to get at him. The incredibly brave cook was actually catching up on the lion and was now not more than ten yards behind him, and Robert Sanford was thirty or forty yards behind the cook. 'Ayee!' the cook was shouting. 'Simba! Simba! Simba! Let go my wife! I am coming after you, simba!'

Then Robert Sanford stopped and raised his rifle and took aim, and I thought surely he is not risking a shot at a moving lion when it's got a woman in its jaws. There was an almighty *crack* as the big gun went off and I saw a spurt of dust just ahead of the lion. The lion stopped dead and turned his head, still holding the woman in his jaws. He saw the arm-waving shouting cook and he saw Robert Sanford and he saw me and he had certainly heard the rifle shot and seen the spurt of dust. He must have thought an army was coming after him because instantaneously he dropped the cook's wife on to the ground and broke for cover. I have never seen anything accelerate so fast from a standing start. With great leaping bounding strides he was in among the jungle trees on the hillock before Robert Sanford could ram another cartridge into his gun.

The cook reached the wife first, then Robert Sanford, then me. I couldn't believe what I saw. I was certain that the grip of those terrible jaws would have ripped the woman's waist and stomach almost in two, but there she was sitting up on the ground and smiling at the cook, her husband.

'Where are you hurt?' shouted Robert Sanford, rushing up.

The cook's wife looked up at him and kept smiling, and she said in Swahili, 'That old lion he couldn't scare me. I just lay there in his mouth pretending I was dead and he didn't even bite through my clothes.' She stood up and smoothed down her red and white spotted dress which was wet with the lion's saliva, and the cook embraced her and the two of them did a little dance of joy in the twilight out there on the great brown African plain.

Robert Sanford just stood there gaping at the cook's wife. So, for that matter, did I.

'Are you absolutely sure the simba didn't hurt you?' he asked her. 'Did not his teeth go into your body?'

'No, bwana,' the woman said, laughing. 'He carried me as gently as if I had been one of his own cubs. But now I shall have to wash my dress.'

We walked slowly back to the group of astonished onlookers. 'Tonight', Robert Sanford said, addressing them all, 'nobody is to go far from the house, you understand me?'

'Yes, bwana,' they said. 'Yes, yes, we understand you.'

'That old simba is hiding over there in the wood and he may come back,' Robert Sanford said. 'So be very careful. And Pingo, please continue to cook our dinner. I am getting hungry.'

The cook ran into the kitchen, clapping his hands and leaping for joy. We walked over to where Mary Sanford was standing. She had come round to the back of the house soon after us and had witnessed the whole scene. The three of us then returned to the veranda and fresh drinks were poured.

Dar es Salaam
5 June 1939

Dear Mama,

It's pleasant lying back and listening to and at the same time watching the antics of Hitler and Mussolini who are invariably on the ceiling catching flys and mosquitoes. Hitler & Mussolini are 2 lizards which live in our sitting room. They're always here, and apart from being very useful about the house they are exciting to watch. You can see Hitler (who is smaller than Musso and not so fat) fixing his unfortunate victim – often a small moth – with a very hypnotic eye. The moth, terrified, stays stock still, then suddenly, so quickly that you can hardly see the movement at all, he darts his neck forward, shoots out a long tongue, and that's the end of the moth. They're quite small only about 10 inches long, and they've taken on the colour of the walls & ceiling which are yellow & become quite transparent. You can see their appendixes, at least we think we can . . .

'I don't believe anything like this has ever happened before,' Robert Sanford said as he sat down once again in his cane armchair. There was a little round slot in one of the arms of the chair to carry his glass and he put the whisky and soda carefully into it. 'In the first place,' he went on, 'lions do not attack people around here unless you go near their cubs. They can get all the food they want. There's plenty of game on the plain.'

'Perhaps he's got a family in that patch of wood on the hill,' Mary Sanford said.

'That could be,' Robert Sanford said. 'But if he had thought the woman was threatening his family, he would have killed her on the spot. Instead of that, he carries her off as soft and gentle as a good gun-dog with a partridge. If you want my opinion, I do not believe he ever meant to hurt her.'

We sat there sipping our drinks and trying to find some sort of an explanation for the astonishing behaviour of the lion.

'Normally,' Robert Sanford said, 'I would get together a bunch of hunters first thing tomorrow morning and we'd flush out that old lion and kill him. But I don't want to do it. He doesn't deserve it. In fact, I'm *not going* to do it.'

'Good for you, darling,' his wife said.

The story of this strange happening with the lion spread in the end all over East Africa and it became a bit of a legend. And when I got back to Dar es Salaam about two weeks later, there was a letter waiting for me from the *East African Standard* (I think it was called) up in Nairobi asking if I would write my own eye-witness description of the incident. This I did and in time I received a cheque for five pounds from the newspaper for my first published work.

There followed a long correspondence in the columns of the paper from the white hunters and other experts all over Uganda, Kenya and Tanganyika, each offering his or her different and often bizarre explanation. But none of them made any sense. The matter has remained a mystery ever since.

The Green Mamba

Oh, those snakes! How I hated them! They were the only fearful thing about Tanganyika, and a newcomer very quickly learnt to identify most of them and to know which were deadly and which were simply poisonous. The killers, apart from the black mambas, were the green mambas, the cobras and the tiny little puff adders that looked very much like small sticks lying motionless in the middle of a dusty path, and so easy to step on.

One Sunday evening I was invited to go and have a sundowner at the house of an Englishman called Fuller who worked in the Customs office in Dar es Salaam. He lived with his wife and two small children in a plain white wooden house that stood alone some way back from the road in a rough grassy piece of ground with coconut trees scattered about. I was walking across the grass towards the house and was about twenty yards away when I saw a large green snake go gliding straight up the veranda steps of Fuller's house and in through the open front door. The brilliant yellowy-green skin and its great size made me certain it was a green mamba, a creature almost as deadly as the black mamba, and for a few seconds I was so startled and dumbfounded and horrified that I froze to the spot. Then I pulled myself together and ran round to the back of the house shouting, 'Mr Fuller! Mr Fuller!'

Mrs Fuller popped her head out of an upstairs window. 'What on earth's the matter?' she said.

'You've got a large green mamba in your front-room!' I shouted. 'I saw it go up the veranda steps and right in through the door!'

'Fred!' Mrs Fuller shouted, turning round. 'Fred! Come here!'

Freddy Fuller's round red face appeared at the window beside his wife. 'What's up?' he asked.

'There's a green mamba in your living-room!' I shouted.

Without hesitation and without wasting time with more questions, he said to me, 'Stay there. I'm going to lower the children down to you one at a time.' He was completely cool and unruffled. He didn't even raise his voice.

A small girl was lowered down to me by her wrists and I was able to catch her easily by the legs. Then came a small boy. Then Freddy Fuller lowered his wife and I caught her by the waist and put her on the ground. Then came Fuller himself. He hung by his hands from the window-sill and when he let go he landed neatly on his two feet.

We stood in a little group on the grass at the back of the house and I told Fuller exactly what I had seen.

The mother was holding the two children by the hand, one on each side of her. They didn't seem to be particularly alarmed.

'What happens now?' I asked.

'Go down to the road, all of you,' Fuller said. 'I'm off to fetch the snake-man.' He trotted away and got into his small ancient black car and drove off. Mrs Fuller and the two small children and I went down to the road and sat in the shade of a large mango tree.

'Who is this snake-man?' I asked Mrs Fuller.

'He is an old Englishman who has been out here for years,' Mrs Fuller said. 'He actually *likes* snakes. He understands them and never kills them. He catches them and sells them to zoos and laboratories all over the world. Every native for miles around knows about him and whenever one of them sees a snake, he marks its hiding place and runs, often for great distances, to tell the snake-man. Then the snake-man comes along and captures it. The snake-man's strict rule is that he will never buy a captured snake from the natives.'

'Why not?' I asked.

'To discourage them from trying to catch snakes themselves,' Mrs Fuller said. 'In his early days he used to buy caught snakes, but so many natives got bitten trying to catch them, and so many died, that he decided to put a stop to it. Now any native who brings in a caught snake, no matter how rare, gets turned away.'

'That's good,' I said.

'What is the snake-man's name?' I asked.

'Donald Macfarlane,' she said. 'I believe he's Scottish.'

'Is the snake in the house, Mummy?' the small girl asked.

'Yes, darling. But the snake-man is going to get it out.'

'He'll bite Jack,' the girl said.

'Oh, my God!' Mrs Fuller cried, jumping to her feet. 'I forgot about Jack!' She began calling out, 'Jack! Come here, Jack! Jack! . . . Jack! . . . Jack!'

The children jumped up as well and all of them started calling to the dog. But no dog came out of the open front door.

'He's bitten Jack!' the small girl cried out. 'He must have bitten him!' She began to cry and so did her brother who was a year or so younger than she was. Mrs Fuller looked grim.

'Jack's probably hiding upstairs,' she said. 'You know how clever he is.'

Mrs Fuller and I seated ourselves again on the grass, but the children remained standing. In between their tears they went on calling to the dog.

'Would you like me to take you down to the Maddens' house?' their mother asked.

'No!' they cried. 'No, no, no! We want Jack!'

'Here's Daddy!' Mrs Fuller cried, pointing at the tiny black car coming up the road in a swirl of dust. I noticed a long wooden pole sticking out through one of the car windows.

The children ran to meet the car. 'Jack's inside the house and he's been bitten by the snake!' they wailed. 'We know he's been bitten! He doesn't come when we call him!'

Mr Fuller and the snake-man got out of the car. The snake-man was small and very old, probably over seventy. He wore leather boots made of thick cowhide and he had long gauntlet-type gloves on his hands made of the same stuff. The gloves reached above his elbows. In his right hand he carried an extraordinary implement, an eight-foot-long wooden pole with a forked end. The two prongs of the fork were made, so it seemed, of black rubber, about an inch thick and quite flexible, and it was clear that if the fork was pressed against the ground the two prongs would bend outwards, allowing the neck of the fork to go down as close to the ground as necessary. In his left hand he carried an ordinary brown sack.

Donald Macfarlane, the snake-man, may have been old and small but he was an impressive-looking character. His eyes were pale blue, deep-set in a face round and dark and wrinkled as a walnut. Above the blue eyes, the eye-brows were thick and startlingly white but the hair on his head was almost black. In spite of the thick leather boots, he moved like a leopard, with soft slow cat-like strides, and he came straight up to me and said, 'Who are you?'

'He's with Shell,' Fuller said. 'He hasn't been here long.'

'You want to watch?' the snake-man said to me.

'Watch?' I said, wavering. 'Watch? How do you mean watch? I mean where from? Not in the house?'

'You can stand out on the veranda and look through the window,' the snake-man said.

'Come on,' Fuller said. 'We'll both watch.'

'Now don't do anything silly,' Mrs Fuller said.

The two children stood there forlorn and miserable, with tears all over their cheeks.

The snake-man and Fuller and I walked over the grass towards the house, and as we approached the veranda steps the snake-man whispered, 'Tread softly on the wooden boards or he'll pick up the vibration. Wait until I've gone in, then walk up quietly and stand by the window.'

The snake-man went up the steps first and he made

absolutely no sound at all with his feet. He moved soft and cat-like on to the veranda and straight through the front door and then he quickly but very quietly closed the door behind him.

I felt better with the door closed. What I mean is I felt better for myself. I certainly didn't feel better for the snake-man. I figured he was committing suicide. I followed Fuller on to the veranda and we both crept over to the window. The window was open, but it had a fine mesh mosquito-netting all over it. That made me feel better still. We peered through the netting.

The living-room was simple and ordinary, coconut matting on the floor, a red sofa, a coffee-table and a couple of armchairs. The dog was sprawled on the matting under the coffee-table, a large Airedale with curly brown and black hair. He was stone dead.

The snake-man was standing absolutely still just inside the door of the living-room. The brown sack was now slung over his left shoulder and he was grasping the long pole with both hands, holding it out in front of him, parallel to the ground. I couldn't see the snake. I didn't think the snake-man had seen it yet either.

A minute went by . . . two minutes . . . three . . . four . . . five. Nobody moved. There was death in that room. The air was heavy with death and the snake-man stood as motionless as a pillar of stone, with the long rod held out in front of him.

And still he waited. Another minute . . . and another . . . and another.

And now I saw the snake-man beginning to bend his

knees. Very slowly he bent his knees until he was almost squatting on the floor, and from that position he tried to peer under the sofa and the armchairs.

And still it didn't look as though he was seeing anything.

Slowly he straightened his legs again, and then his head began to swivel around the room. Over to the right, in the far corner, a staircase led up to the floor above. The snake-man looked at the stairs, and I knew very well what was going through his head. Quite abruptly, he took one step forward and stopped.

Nothing happened.

A moment later I caught sight of the snake. It was lying full-length along the skirting of the right-hand wall, but hidden from the snake-man's view by the back of the sofa. It lay there like a long, beautiful, deadly shaft of green glass, quite motionless, perhaps asleep. It was facing away from us who were at the window, with its small triangular head resting on the matting near the foot of the stairs.

I nudged Fuller and whispered, 'It's over there against the wall.' I pointed and Fuller saw the snake. At once, he started waving both hands, palms outward, back and forth across the window hoping to get the snake-man's attention. The snake-man didn't see him. Very softly, Fuller said, 'Pssst!', and the snake-man looked up sharply. Fuller pointed. The snake-man understood and gave a nod.

Now the snake-man began working his way very very slowly to the back wall of the room so as to get a view of the snake behind the sofa. He never walked on his toes as you or I would have done. His feet remained flat on the ground all the time. The cowhide boots were like moccasins, with neither soles nor heels. Gradually, he worked his way over to the back wall, and from there he was able to see at least the head and two or three feet of the snake itself.

But the snake also saw him. With a movement so fast it was invisible, the snake's head came up about two feet off the floor and the front of the body arched backwards, ready to strike. Almost simultaneously, it bunched its whole body into a series of curves, ready to flash forward.

The snake-man was just a bit too far away from the snake to reach it with the end of his pole. He waited, staring at the snake and the snake stared back at him with two small malevolent black eyes.

Then the snake-man started speaking to the snake. 'Come along, my pretty,' he whispered in a soft wheedling voice. 'There's a good boy. Nobody's going to hurt you. Nobody's going to harm you, my pretty little thing. Just lie still and relax . . .' He took a step forward towards the snake, holding the pole out in front of him.

What the snake did next was so fast that the whole movement couldn't have taken more than a hundredth of a second, like the flick of a camera shutter. There was a green flash as the snake darted forward at least ten feet and struck at the snake-man's leg. Nobody could have got out of the way of that one. I heard the snake's head strike against the thick cowhide boot with a sharp little *crack*, and then at once the head was back in that same deadly backward-curving position, ready to strike again.

'There's a good boy,' the snake-man said softly. 'There's a clever boy. There's a lovely fellow. You mustn't get excited. Keep calm and everything's going to be all right.' As he was speaking, he was slowly lowering the end of the pole until the forked prongs were about twelve inches above the middle of the snake's body. 'There's a lovely fellow,' he whispered. 'There's a good kind little chap. Keep still now, my beauty. Keep still, my pretty. Keep quite still. Daddy's not going to hurt you.'

I could see a thin dark trickle of venom running down the snake-man's right boot where the snake had struck.

The snake, head raised and arcing backwards, was as tense as a tight-wound spring and ready to strike again. 'Keep still, my lovely,' the snake-man whispered. 'Don't move now. Keep still. No one's going to hurt you.'

Then *wham*, the rubber prongs came down right across the snake's body, about midway along its length, and pinned it to the floor. All I could see was a green blur as the snake thrashed around furiously in an effort to free itself. But the snake-man kept up the pressure on the prongs and the snake was trapped.

What happens next? I wondered. There was no way he could catch hold of that madly twisting flailing length of green muscle with his hands, and even if he could have done so, the head would surely have flashed around and bitten him in the face.

Holding the very end of the eight-foot pole, the snake-man began to work his way round the room until he was at the tail end of the snake. Then, in spite of the flailing and the thrashing, he started pushing the prongs forward along the snake's body towards the head. Very very slowly he did it, pushing the rubber prongs forward over the snake's flailing body, keeping the snake pinned down all the time and pushing, pushing, pushing the long wooden rod forward millimetre by millimetre. It was a fascinating and frightening thing to watch, the little man with white eyebrows and black hair carefully manipulating his long implement and sliding the fork ever so slowly along the length of the twisting snake towards the head. The snake's body was thumping against the coconut matting with such a noise that if you had been upstairs you might have thought two big men were wrestling on the floor.

Then at last the prongs were right behind the head itself, pinning it down, and at that point the snake-man reached forward with one gloved hand and grasped the snake very firmly by the neck. He threw away the pole. He took the sack off his shoulder with his free hand. He lifted the great, still-twisting length of the deadly green snake and pushed the head into the sack. Then he let go the head and bundled the rest of the creature in and closed the sack. The sack started jumping about as though there were fifty angry rats inside it, but the snake-man was now totally relaxed and he held the sack casually in one hand as if it contained no more than a few pounds of potatoes. He stooped and picked up his pole from the floor, then he turned and looked towards the window where we were peering in.

'Pity about the dog,' he said. 'You'd better get it out of the way before the children see it.'

Green Mamba !

The Beginning of the War

Breakfast in Dar es Salaam never varied. It was always a delicious ripe pawpaw picked that morning in the garden by the cook, on to which was squeezed the juice of a whole fresh lime. Just about every white man and woman in Tanganyika had pawpaw and lime juice for breakfast, and I believe those old colonials knew what was good for them. It is the healthiest and most refreshing breakfast I know.

On a morning towards the end of August 1939, I was breakfasting on my pawpaw and thinking a great deal, like everyone else, about the war that we all knew was very soon going to break out with Germany. Mdisho was moving around the room and pretending to be busy.

'Did you know there is going to be a war before very long?' I asked him.

'A war?' he cried, perking up immediately. 'A real war, bwana?'

'An enormous war,' I said.

Mdisho's face was now alight with excitement. He was of the Mwanumwezi tribe and there wasn't a Mwanumwezi anywhere who did not have fighting in his blood. For hundreds of years they had been the greatest warriors in East Africa, conquering all before them, including the Masai, and even now the mere mention of war caused such dreams of glory in Mdisho's mind that he could hardly stand it.

'I still have my father's weapons in my hut!' he cried. 'I shall get the spear out and start sharpening it immediately! Who are we going to fight, bwana?'

'The Germani,' I said.

'Good,' he said. 'There are plenty of Germani around here for us to kill.'

Mdisho was right about there being plenty of them. Only twenty-five years ago, before the First World War, Tanganyika had been German East Africa. But in 1919 after the Armistice, Germany had been forced to hand the territory over to the British, who renamed it Tanganyika. Many Germans had stayed on and the country was still full of them. They owned diamond mines and gold mines. They grew sisal and cotton and tea and ground-nuts. The owner of the soda-water bottling-plant in Dar es Salaam was a German and so was Willy Hink, the watchmaker. In fact the Germans greatly outnumbered all the other Europeans in Tanganyika put together, and when war broke out, as we now knew it must, they could present a dangerous and difficult problem to the authorities.

'When is this enormous war going to begin?' Mdisho asked me.

'They say quite soon,' I told him, 'because over in Europe, which is ten times as far away as from here to Kilimanjaro, the Germans have a leader called Bwana Hitler who wishes to conquer the world. The Germans think this Bwana Hitler is a wonderful fellow. But he is actually a raving mad maniac. As soon as the war begins, the Germani will try to kill us all, and then, of course, we shall have to try to kill them before they can kill us.'

Mdisho, being a true child of his tribe, understood the principle of war very well. 'Why don't we strike first?' he said, excitedly. 'Why don't we take them by surprise, these Germani out here, bwana? Why don't we kill all of them *before* the war begins? That is always the best way, bwana. My ancestors always used to strike first.'

'I am afraid we have very strict rules about war,' I said. 'With us, nobody is allowed to kill anyone until the whistle blows and the game is officially started.'

'But that is ridiculous, bwana!' he cried. 'In a war there are no rules! Winning is all that counts!'

Mdisho was only nineteen years old. He had been born and brought up 700 miles inland from Dar es Salaam, near a place called Kigoma, on the shores of Lake Tanganyika, and both his parents had died before he was twelve years old. He had then been taken into the household of a kindly District Officer in Kigoma and given the job of assistant shamba-boy or gardener. From there he had graduated into the household as a house-boy and had charmed everybody by his good manners and gentle bearing. When the District Officer had been moved back to the Secretariat in Dar es Salaam, the family had taken Mdisho with them. A year or so later, the DO had been transferred to Egypt and poor Mdisho was suddenly without a job or a home, but he did have in his possession one very valuable document, a splendid reference from his former employer. That was when I was lucky enough to find him and take him on. I made him my personal 'boy' and soon the two of us had formed a friendship that I found rather marvellous.

Mdisho could neither read nor write, and it was impossible for him to imagine that the world extended much beyond the shores of the African continent. But he was undoubtedly intelligent and quick to learn, and I had begun to teach him how to read. Every weekday, as soon as I got home from the office, we would have three-quarters of an hour of reading. He learnt fast, and although we were still on single words, we would soon be progressing to short sentences. I insisted on teaching him how to read and write not only Swahili words but also their English equivalents, so that he would learn a little basic English at the same time. He loved his lessons and it was touching to see him already seated at the table in the dining-room with his exercise book open in front of him when I came home in the evenings.

Mdisho was about six feet tall, superbly built, with a rather scrunched-up flat-nosed face and the most beautiful pure white absolutely even teeth I had ever seen.

'It is most important to obey the rules of war,' I told him. 'No Germani can be killed until war has been properly declared. And even then the enemy must be given the chance to surrender before you kill him.'

'How will we know when war is declared?' Mdisho asked me.

'They will tell us on the wireless from England,' I said. 'We shall all know within a few seconds.'

'And then the fun will begin!' he cried, clapping his hands. 'Oh bwana, I can hardly wait for that time to come!'

'If you want to fight, you must become a soldier first,' I told him. 'You will have to join the Kenya Regiment and become an askari.' An askari was a soldier in the King's African Rifles, the KAR.

'The askaris have guns and I don't know how to use a gun,' he said.

'They will teach you,' I said. 'You might enjoy it.'

'That would be a very serious step for me to take, bwana,' he said. 'I shall have to give it a great deal of thought.'

A few days after that, things started hotting up in Dar es Salaam. War was clearly imminent, and elaborate plans were made to round up the hundreds of Germans in Dar es Salaam and upcountry as soon as war was declared. There were not a lot of young Englishmen in Dar, perhaps fifteen or twenty at the most, and all of us were ordered to leave our jobs and to become, by some magic process, temporary army officers. I was given a red armband and a platoon of askaris to command, but never having been a soldier in my life, except at school, I felt rather at a loss with twenty-five highly trained troops with rifles and one machine-gun in my charge.

> *Dar es Salaam*
> *Sunday, no date*

Dear Mama,

Last week I finally succumbed to Malaria and went to bed on Wednesday night with the most terrific head and a temp of 103°. Next day it was 104° and on Friday 105°. They've got some marvellous new stuff called Atebrin which they straightway inject into your bottom in vast quantities which suddenly brings the temperature down; then they give you an injection of 15 or 20 grams of quinine and by that time you haven't got any bottom left at all – one side's just Atebrin and the other's quinine.

I suppose that by the time you get this letter war will either be declared or it'll be off, but at the moment things, even here, are humming a bit. We're all temporary army officers, with batons, belts & all sorts of secret instructions. If we go out of the house we've got to leave word where we've gone to so that we can be called at a moment's notice. We know exactly where to go if anything happens but everything's very secret, and as I'm not sure whether our letters are being censored or not I'm not going to tell you any more. But if war breaks out it'll be our job to round up all the Germans here, and after that things ought to be pretty quiet . . .

I was summoned to the army barracks in Dar es Salaam where a British Captain in the KAR gave me my orders. He was seated at a wooden table with his hat on in a swelteringly hot tin hut, and he had a little clipped brown moustache that kept jumping about when he spoke.

'As soon as war is declared,' he said, 'all male Germans must be rounded up at the point of a gun and put into the prison camp. The prison camp is ready, and the Germans know it is ready, so many of them will try to escape from the country before we can catch them. The nearest neutral territory is Portuguese East Africa, and there is only one road running there from Dar es Salaam, the coast road going south. Do you know it?'

Dar es Salaam
Friday 15 Sept

Dear Mama,

I'm very sorry I haven't written to you for such ages but you can guess that things have been humming a bit here. Now all the Germans in the Territory, and it's a pretty big place in which to try to catch them, have been safely put inside an internment camp. And we army officers were the people who had to collect them. The moment that war broke out at about 1.15 p.m. on Sunday the alarm was given on a series of telephones and certain key men dashed round and collected their squads, & proceeded to the police lines to be armed and to receive orders. At the time, I was actually out guarding the road going down the South Coast to Kilwa and Lindi with native troops (Askaris) and a blockade across the road. All I heard was a grim voice down the field telephone which said, 'War has been declared – standby – arrest all Germans attempting to leave or enter the town.' Then the fun started. I better not say any more or the censor might hold up the letter ...

I told him I knew it very well.

'Down that road', the Captain said, 'every German in Dar es Salaam will try to run the moment war is declared. It will be your duty to stop them and round them up and bring them back to the prison camp.'

'Who, *me*?' I cried, aghast.

'You and your platoon,' he said. 'We can't spare any more men. We've got the entire country to cover. Make sure you take up a sensible defensive position and deploy your troops under good cover. Some of those Germans may try to shoot their way out.'

'You mean', I said, 'that just me and my platoon are going to try to stop every German in Dar?'

'Those are your orders,' he said.

'But there must be hundreds of them.'

'There are,' he said, smirking a bit.

'What happens if they *do* have guns and put up a fight?' I asked.

'Mow them down,' the Captain said. 'You've got a machine-gun, haven't you? One machine-gun can defeat 500 men with rifles.'

I was getting nervous. I didn't want to be the person who gave the order to mow down 500 civilians out there on the dusty coast road that led to Portuguese East Africa. 'What happens if they've got their women and children with them?' I asked.

'You'll have to use your discretion,' the Captain said, evading the issue.

'But ... but,' I stammered, 'that road is the most important escape route in the whole country. Don't you think that you or some other regular officer should be doing this job?'

'We've all got our hands full,' the Captain said.

I tried once more. 'I am really not trained for this sort of thing,' I said. 'I'm just a chap who works for Shell.'

'Rubbish!' he barked. 'Off you go now! And don't let us down!'

So off I went.

I found a telephone and called Mdisho at the house to tell him not to expect me back until he saw me.

'I know where you are going, bwana!' he shouted down the phone. 'You are going after the Germani! Am I right?'

'Well,' I said, 'we'll see.'

'Let me come with you, bwana!' he cried. 'Oh, *please* let me come with you!'

'I'm afraid that's not possible this time, Mdisho,' I said. 'You'll just have to stay and look after the house.'

'Be careful, bwana,' he said. 'You *will* be careful they do not kill you.'

I went out into the barrack square where my platoon was waiting for me. The askaris looked very smart in their khaki shorts and shirts, and they were lined up at attention beside two open trucks with their rifles at their sides. As soon as I arrived, the Sergeant saluted me and told the men to get into the trucks. I sat in the cabin of the front truck between the driver and the Sergeant, and we drove through the town towards the coast road that would lead eventually to Mozambique in Portuguese East Africa. In the second truck the askaris had a huge reel of telephone cable which they were going to lay along our route so that I could keep in touch with headquarters and be told the moment war was declared. There were no radios for that sort of thing out there.

'How much cable have you got?' I asked the Sergeant. 'How far along the road can we go?'

'Only about three miles, bwana,' he answered, grinning.

Just outside Dar es Salaam we stopped by a small hut and two signallers jumped out and unlocked the door and connected up our telephone cable to a plug inside. Then we drove on and the signallers fed the telephone cable out on to the grass verge as we went slowly forward. The road ran right along the edge of the Indian Ocean, and the water out there was calm and clear and pale green. I could see the sandy bottom under the water for a long way out and on the little strip of sand between us and the water there grew those everlasting coconut palms waving their tops high up against the hot blue sky. It was a very beautiful sight and a little breeze was blowing from the sea into the cabin of our truck.

After a couple of miles, we came to a place where the road sloped steeply uphill and curved inland and went right through some very thick jungle. 'What about over there in the trees?' I asked the Sergeant.

'It is a good place,' he said, so we stopped where the road entered the jungle and we climbed out of the trucks.

'Leave the trucks outside blocking the road,' I said to the Sergeant, 'and see that each man takes up a concealed position on the edge of the forest. The machine-gun and all the rifles must be able to cover the road just beyond the blockade.'

When all this had been done, I took the Sergeant aside and had a little talk with him in Swahili. 'Look, Sergeant,' I said, 'I am sure you realize that I am not a soldier.'

'I realize that, bwana,' he said politely.

'So if you see me doing something silly, please tell me.'

'Yes, bwana,' he said.

'Are you happy with our positions?' I asked him.

'I think everything is fine, bwana,' he said.

So we hung around through the afternoon waiting for

the field telephone to ring. I sat on the ground in a shady place near the phone and smoked my pipe. I remember I was wearing a khaki shirt, khaki shorts, khaki stockings and brown shoes, and I had a khaki topee on my head. That was the regular civilian way of dressing out there and very comfortable it was. But I myself was far from comfortable in my mind. I was twenty-three and I had not yet been trained to kill anyone. I wasn't absolutely sure that I could bring myself to give the order to open fire on a bunch of German civilians in cold blood should the necessity arise. I was feeling altogether very uncomfortable in my skin.

Darkness came and still the telephone did not ring.

There was a 44-gallon drum of drinking water in one of the trucks and everyone helped himself. Then the Sergeant made a fire out of sticks and began cooking supper for his men. He was making rice in an enormous pot, and while the rice was boiling he took from the truck a great stem of bananas and started snapping them off the stem one by one and peeling them and slicing them up and dropping the slices into the pot of rice. When the food was ready, each askari produced his own tin plate and spoon and the Sergeant dished out large portions with a ladle. Up to then I hadn't thought about my own food and I certainly had not brought anything with me. Watching the men eat made me hungry. 'Do you think I could have a little of that, please?' I said to the Sergeant.

'Yes, bwana,' he said. 'Have you got a plate?'

'No,' I said. So he found me a tin plate and a spoon and gave me a huge helping. It was absolutely delicious. The rice was unhusked and brown and the grains did not stick together. The slices of banana were hot and sweet and in some way they oiled the rice, as butter would. It was the best rice dish I had ever tasted and I ate it all and felt good and forgot about the Germans. 'Wonderful,' I said to the Sergeant. 'You are a fine cook.'

'Whenever we are out of the barracks,' he said, 'I must feed my men. It is something you have to learn when you become a Sergeant.'

'It was truly magnificent,' I said. 'You should open a restaurant and become rich.'

All around us in the forest the frogs were croaking incessantly. African frogs have an unusually loud rasping croak and however far away from you they are, the sound always seems to be coming from somewhere near your feet. The croaking of frogs is the night music of the East African coast. The actual croak is made only by the bull-frog and he does it by blowing out his dewlap and letting it go with a *burp*. This is his mating call and when the female hears it she hops smartly over to the side of her prospective mate. But when she arrives a curious thing happens and it is not quite what you are thinking. The bullfrog does not turn and greet the female. Far from it. He ignores her totally and continues to sit there singing his song to the stars while the female waits patiently beside him. She waits and she waits and she waits. The male sings and he sings and he sings, often for several hours, and what has actually happened is this. The bull-frog has fallen so much in love with the sound of his own voice that he has completely forgotten why he started croaking in the first place. *We* know that he started because he was feeling sexy. But now he has become mesmerized by the lovely music he is making so that for him nothing else exists, not even the panting female at his side. There comes a time, though, when she loses all patience and starts nudging him hard with a foreleg, and only then does the bullfrog come out of his trance and turn to embrace her.

Ah well. The bullfrog, I told myself as I sat there in the dark forest, is not after all so very different from a lot of human males that I could think of.

I borrowed an army blanket from the Sergeant and settled down for the night beside the telephone. I thought briefly about snakes and wondered how many there were gliding about on the floor of the forest. Probably thousands. But the askaris were chancing it so why shouldn't I?

The phone did not ring in the night and at dawn the Sergeant built his fire again and cooked us some more rice and bananas. It didn't taste so good early in the morning.

Shortly after eleven o'clock the tinkle of the field telephone made everybody jump. The voice on the other end said to me, 'Great Britain has declared war on Germany. You are now on full alert.' Then he rang off. I told the Sergeant to get all his men into their positions.

For an hour or so nothing happened. The askaris waited behind their guns and I waited out in the open beside the two trucks that were blocking the road.

Then, suddenly, away in the distance I saw a cloud of

dust. A little later, I could make out the first car, then close behind it a second and a third and a fourth. All the Germans in Dar must have made arrangements to assemble and travel together in convoy as soon as war was declared, for now I could see a line of cars, each about twenty yards behind the one in front, stretching for half a mile down the road. There were trucks piled high with baggage. There were ordinary saloons with pieces of furniture strapped on their roofs. There were vans and there were station-wagons. I called the Sergeant out of the forest. 'Here they come,' I said, 'and there's plenty of them. I want you to stay out of sight with the men. I shall remain here and meet the Germans. If I raise two arms above my head, like this, the machine-gun and all the rifles are to fire one burst over the heads of these people. Not *at* them, you understand, but over their heads.'

'Yes, bwana, one burst over their heads.'

'If there is violence towards me and they try to force their way through, then you will be in charge and must do whatever you think right.'

'Yes, bwana,' the Sergeant said, relishing the possibility. He returned to the forest. I stood out on the road waiting for the leader of the convoy to reach me. The lead car was a large Chevrolet station-wagon driven by a man who had two more men beside him in the front seat. The rest of the car was filled with baggage. I put one hand up for him to stop, which he did. I felt like a traffic cop as I strolled over to the driver's window.

'I am afraid you cannot go any further,' I said. 'You and all the others must turn around and go back to Dar es

Salaam. One of my trucks will lead you. The other will bring up the rear of the convoy.'

'Vot sort of bull is this?' the man shouted with a heavy German accent. He was middle-aged with a thick neck and he was almost bald. 'Move those trucks off the road! Vi are going through!'

'I'm afraid not,' I said. 'You are now prisoners of war.'

The bald man got slowly out of the car. He was very angry and his movements were full of menace. The two men with him also got out. The bald man turned and signalled with his arm to the fifty-odd cars that were lined up behind him, and immediately a man, and sometimes two, got out of each car and came walking towards us. There were women and children in many of the cars as well, but they stayed where they were.

I didn't at all like the way things were shaping up. What *was* I going to do, I asked myself, if they refused to go back and tried to barge their way through? I knew there and then that I could never quite bring myself to give the order for the machine-gun to mow them all down. It would be an appalling massacre. I stood there and said nothing.

In a few minutes a crowd of not less than seventy Germans were standing in a half-circle behind the bald man, who was clearly their leader.

The bald man turned away from me and addressed his countrymen. 'OK,' he said. 'Let's get these two trucks off the road and move on.'

'Hold it!' I said, trying to sound twice my age. 'I have orders to stop you at all costs. If you try to go on, we shall shoot.'

'Who vill shoot?' asked the bald man contemptuously. He drew a revolver from the back pocket of his khaki trousers and I saw that it was one of those long-barrelled Lugers. Immediately, at least half of the seventy or so men standing around him produced identical weapons. The bald man pointed his Luger at my chest.

I had seen this sort of thing done a thousand times in the cinema, but it was a very different thing in real life. I was properly frightened. I did my best not to show it. Then I raised both arms above my head. The bald man smiled. He thought it was a gesture of surrender.

Crack! Crack! Crack! All the guns behind me including the machine-gun opened up and bullets went whistling over our heads. The Germans jumped. They quite literally jumped. Even the bald man jumped. And so did I.

I lowered my hands. 'There is no way you can get through,' I said. 'The first man who tries to go on from here will be shot. If all of you try, then all of you will be shot. Those are my orders. I have enough fire-power in there to stop a regiment.'

There was absolute silence. The bald man lowered his Luger and suddenly his whole attitude changed. He gave me an ugly forced smile and said softly, 'Vy do you not let us through?'

'Because we are at war with Germany,' I said, 'and you are all of German nationality, therefore you are the enemy.'

'Vi are civilians,' he said.

'Maybe you are,' I said. 'But as soon as you get to

Portuguese East, you'll find your way back to the Fatherland and become soldiers. You are not going through.'

Suddenly he grabbed my arm and put his Luger to my chest. Then he raised his voice and screamed to my invisible troops in Swahili, 'If you try to stop us I am going to shoot your officer!'

What came next happened very suddenly. There was the *crack* of a single rifle shot fired from the wood and the bald man who was holding me took the bullet right through his face. It was a horrible sight. The Luger dropped on to the road and the bald man fell dead beside it.

All of us were shaken up, but I managed to pull myself together enough to say, 'Come on, let us not have any more killings. Turn your vehicles round and follow our lead truck back to town. You will be well treated and the women and children will be allowed to go home.'

The crowd of men turned and walked sullenly back towards their cars.

'Sergeant!' I shouted and the Sergeant came out of the forest at the double. 'Put the dead man in one of the trucks and take it to the head of the convoy,' I said to him. 'You go with the front truck and lead them all to the prison camp. I shall bring up the rear in the second truck.'

'Very well, bwana,' the Sergeant said.

And that was how we captured the German civilians in Dar es Salaam when the war broke out.

Mdisho of the Mwanumwezi

By the time we had seen the Germans safely into the prison camp and I had made my report, it was nearly midnight. I went off home to get a shower and some sleep. I was tired and dirty and I was feeling very unhappy about the killing of the bald-headed German. The Captain at the barracks had congratulated me and said it was exactly the right thing to do, but that didn't help.

When I got home, I went straight upstairs and took off my clothes. I took a long shower, then I put on a pair of pyjamas and went downstairs again for a badly needed whisky and soda.

In the living-room I lay back in my armchair sipping the whisky and ruminating upon the strange events of the last thirty-six hours. The whisky felt good and I was slowly beginning to relax as the alcohol got into the blood-stream. Through the wide-open french windows I could hear the Indian Ocean pounding the cliffs below the house and as always when I sat in that chair, I turned my head a little in order to allow my eyes to rest upon my beautiful silver Arab sword that hung on the wall over the door. I nearly dropped my whisky. The sword was gone. The scabbard was still there but the sword itself was not in it.

I had bought my sword about a year before from the Captain of an Arab dhow in Dar es Salaam harbour. This Captain had sailed his old dhow clear across from Muscat to Africa on the north-east monsoon and the journey had taken him thirty-four days. I happened to be down in the harbour when she came sailing in and I gladly accepted the invitation of the Customs Officer to accompany him on board. That is where I found the sword and fell in love with it at first sight and bought it from the Captain on the spot for 500 shillings.

The sword was long and curved and the silver scabbard was wonderfully chased with an intricate design showing various phases in the life of the Prophet. The curved blade was over three feet in length and was as sharp as a well-honed chisel. My friends in Dar es Salaam who knew about such things told me it was almost certainly from the middle of the eighteenth century and should properly be in a museum.

I had carried my treasure back to the house and had handed it to Mdisho. 'I want you to hang it on the wall over the door,' I told him. 'And I shall hold you responsible for seeing that the silver scabbard is always polished and the blade is wiped with an oily rag once a week to prevent it from rusting.'

Mdisho took the sword from me and examined it with reverence. Then he drew the blade from the scabbard and tested the edge with his thumb. 'Ayee!' he cried out. 'What a weapon! I could win a war with this in my hand!'

And now I sat in my armchair in the living-room with my whisky, staring appalled at the empty scabbard.

'Mdisho!' I shouted. 'Come here! Where is my sword?' There was no answer. He was probably in bed. I got up and went out to the back of the house where the native quarters were. There was a half-moon in the sky and plenty of stars and I could see Piggy the cook squatting outside his hut with one of his wives.

'Piggy,' I said, 'where is Mdisho?'

Piggy was old and wrinkled, and he was very good at making baked potato with crabmeat inside. He stood up when he saw me and his woman disappeared into the shadows.

'Where is Mdisho?' I said.

'Mdisho went away early in the evening, bwana.'

'Where to?'

'I do not know. But he said he was coming back. Perhaps he has gone to see his father. You were away in the jungle and I expect he thought you would not mind if he went off to pay a call on his father.'

'Where is my sword, Piggy?'

'Your sword, bwana? Is it not hanging over the door?'

'It's gone,' I said. 'I'm afraid someone may have stolen it. The big french windows into the sitting-room were wide open when I came in. That is not right.'

'No bwana, that is not right. I don't understand it at all.'

'Nor do I,' I said. 'Go to bed.'

I went back into the house and flopped down again into the armchair. I felt too tired to move any more. It was a very hot night. I reached up and switched off the reading light, then I closed my eyes and dozed off.

I don't know how long I slept, but when I woke up it was still night and Mdisho was standing just inside the french windows with the light of the half-moon shining down on him from behind. He was breathing fast and there was a wild ecstatic look on his face and he was naked except for a small pair of black cotton shorts. His superb black body was literally dripping with sweat. In his right hand he held the sword.

I sat up abruptly.

'Mdisho, where have you been?' Little flashes of moonlight were glinting on the sword and I noticed that the middle of the blade was darkened with something that looked to me very much like dried blood.

'Mdisho!' I cried. 'For heaven's sake what have you done?'

'Bwana,' he said, 'oh bwana, I have had a most tremendous victory. I think you will be very pleased about it when I tell you.'

'Tell me,' I said. I was getting nervous.

I had never seen Mdisho like this before. The wild look on his face and the heavy breathing and the sweat all over his body made me more nervous than ever. 'Tell me at once,' I said again. 'Explain to me what you have been doing.'

When he started to speak, the words came rushing out in a cascade of crazy excited sentences, and he didn't stop until he had finished his story. I didn't interrupt him, and I will try to give you a fairly literal translation from the Swahili of what he said as he stood there looking so splendid in the open doorway with the half-moon shining on him from behind.

'Bwana,' he said, 'bwana, yesterday down in the market I heard that we had started to fight the Germani and I remembered all that you had said about how they would try to kill us. As soon as I heard the news, I started to run back to the house, and as I ran I shouted to everyone I saw in the streets. I shouted, "We are fighting the Germani! We are fighting the Germani!"

'In my country, as soon as we hear that someone is coming to fight us, the whole tribe must know about it as soon as possible. So I ran home shouting the news to the people as I went, and I was also thinking of what I, Mdisho, could do to help. Suddenly, I remembered the rich Germani that lives over the hills, the sisal planter whom we visited in your car not long ago.

'Then I ran even faster towards home, and when I arrived I ran through the kitchen and shouted at Piggy the cook, "We are fighting the Germani!" I ran into this room and took hold of the sword, this wonderful sword which I have been polishing for you every day.

'Bwana, I was very excited to be at war. You were already out with the askari on the roads, and I knew that I should do something too.

'So I pulled the sword out of its glove and ran outside with it. I ran towards the house of the rich sisal-owning Germani over the hills.

'I did not go by the road because the askaris might have stopped me when they saw me running with the sword in my hand. I ran straight through the forest and when I got to the top of the hills, I looked down the other side and saw the great plantation of sisal belonging to the rich Germani. Away beyond it I could see his house, the big white house we visited together, and I set off again down the other side of the hill into the sisal.

'By then it was getting dark and it was not easy dodging around the tall prickly sisal plants, but I went on running.

'Then I saw the white house in front of me in the moonlight and I ran straight up to the front door and pushed it open. I ran into the first room I saw and it was empty. There was a table with some food on it but the room was empty. Then I ran towards the back of the house and pushed open a door at the end of the passage. That was empty too, but suddenly through the window I saw the big Germani standing in the back garden and he had a fire going and he was throwing pieces of paper on to the fire. He had many sheets of paper on the ground beside him and he kept picking up more and more and throwing them on to the fire. And bwana, there was a huge elephant gun lying on the ground by his feet.

'I pushed open the back door and I ran out and the Germani heard me and jumped round and started to reach for the gun but I gave him no time. I had the sword raised in both my hands and I swung it at his neck as he bent down to pick up the gun.

'Bwana, it is a beautiful sword. With one blow it cut through his neck so deeply that his whole head fell forward and dangled down on to his chest, and as he started to topple over I gave the neck one more quick chop and the head came right away from the body and fell to the ground like a coconut.

'I felt good then, bwana, I really felt awfully good, and I remember wishing I had had you with me to see it all happening. But you were far away on the coast road with your askaris doing the same sort of thing to lots of other Germani, so I hurried home. I came home by the road because it was faster and I didn't care any more about the askaris seeing me. I ran all the way and the sword was in my hand and sometimes I waved it above my head as I ran, but I never stopped. Twice people shouted at me and once two men ran after me, but I was flying like a bird and I was bringing good news back home.

'It is a long distance, bwana, and it took four hours each way. That is why I am so late. I am sorry to be so late.'

Mdisho stopped. He had finished his story. I knew it was true. The German sisal-owner was called Fritz Kleiber and he was a wealthy and extremely unpleasant bachelor. It was rumoured that he treated his workers badly and had been known to beat them with a sjambok, which is a murderous whip made of rhinoceros hide. I wondered why he hadn't been rounded up by our people before Mdisho got to him. They were probably on the way out there now. They were in for a shock.

'And *you*, bwana!' Mdisho cried out. 'How many did *you* get today?'

'How many what?' I said.

'Germani, bwana, Germani! How many did you get with that fine machine-gun you had out on the road?'

I looked at him and smiled. I refused to blame him for what he had done. He was a wild Mwanumwezi tribesman who had been moulded by us Europeans into the shape of a domestic servant, and now he had broken the mould.

'Have you told anyone else what you have done?'

'Not yet, bwana, I came to you first.'

'Now listen carefully,' I said. 'You must tell nobody about this, not your father, not your wives, not your best friend and not Piggy the cook. Do you understand me?'

'But I *must* tell them!' he cried. 'You cannot take that pleasure away from me, bwana!'

'You must *not* tell them, Mdisho,' I said.

'But why not?' he cried. 'Have I done something wrong?'

'Quite the opposite,' I lied.

'Then why must I not tell my people?' he asked again.

I tried to explain to him how the authorities would react if they found him out. It simply wasn't done to go round chopping heads off civilians, even in wartime. It could mean prison, I told him, or even worse than that.

He couldn't believe me. He was absolutely shattered.

'I myself am tremendously proud of you,' I said, trying to make him feel better. 'To me you are a great hero.'

'But *only* to you, bwana?'

'No, Mdisho. I think you would be a hero to most of the British people here if they knew what you had done. But that doesn't help. It is the police who would go after you.'

'The police!' he cried in horror. If there was one thing in Dar es Salaam that every local was terrified of, it was the police. The police constables were all blacks, acting under a couple of white officers at the top, and they were not famous for being gentle with prisoners.

'Yes,' I said, 'the police.' I felt pretty sure they would charge Mdisho with murder if they caught him.

l To r: Mdisho, Piggy, Owino, M Toto, Shamba Boy

'If it is the police, then I will keep quiet, bwana,' he said, and all of a sudden he looked so downcast and disillusioned and defeated that I couldn't bear it. I got up from the chair and crossed the room and took the scabbard of the sword down from the wall. 'I shall be leaving you very soon,' I said. 'I have decided to join the war as a flier of aeroplanes.' The only word for aeroplane in the Swahili language is *ndegi*, which means bird, and it always sounded good and descriptive in a sentence. 'I am going to fly birds,' I said. 'I shall fly English birds against the birds of the Germani.'

'Wonderful!' Mdisho cried, brightening again suddenly at the mention of war. 'I will come with you, bwana.'

'Sadly, that will be impossible,' I said. 'In the beginning

I shall be nothing but a very humble bird-soldier of the lowest rank, like your most junior askaris here, and I shall be living in barracks. There would be no question of me being allowed to have somebody to help me. I shall have to do everything for myself, including the washing and ironing of my shirts.'

'That would be absolutely impossible, bwana,' Mdisho said. He was genuinely shocked.

'I shall manage quite well,' I told him.

'But do you *know* how to iron a shirt, bwana?'

'No,' I said. 'You must teach me that secret before I go.'

'Will it be very dangerous, bwana, where you are going, and do those Germani birds have many guns?'

'It might be dangerous,' I said, 'but the first six months will be nothing but fun. It takes six months for them to teach you how to fly a bird.'

'Where will you go?' he asked.

'First to Nairobi,' I answered. 'They will start us on very small birds in Nairobi, and then we will go somewhere else to fly the big ones. We shall be travelling a great deal with very little luggage. That is why I shall have to leave this sword behind. It would be impossible to carry a great big thing like this with me wherever I go. So I am giving it to you.'

'To me!' he cried. 'Oh no, bwana, you mustn't do that! You will need it where you are going!'

'Not in a bird,' I said. 'There is no room to swing a sword when you are sitting in one of those.' I handed him the beautiful curved silver scabbard. 'You have earned it,' I said. 'Now go away and wash the blade very well indeed.

Make sure there is no trace of blood left on it anywhere. Then wipe it with oil and return it to its glove. Tomorrow I shall hand you a chit saying that I have given it to you. The chit is important.'

He stood there holding the sword in one hand and the scabbard in the other, staring at them with eyes as bright as two stars.

'I am presenting it to you for bravery,' I said. 'But you must not tell that to anybody. Tell them simply that I gave it to you as a going-away present.'

'Yes, bwana,' he said. 'That is what I shall tell them.' He paused for a moment and looked me straight in the eye. 'Tell me truthfully, bwana,' he said, 'are you really and truly glad that I killed the big Germani sisal-grower?'

'*We* killed one today as well,' I said.

'You *did*?' Mdisho cried. 'You killed one, too?'

'We had to do it or he would probably have killed me.'

'Then we are equal, bwana,' he said, smiling with his wonderful white teeth. 'That makes us exactly equal, you and me.'

'Yes,' I said. 'I suppose it does.'

Flying Training

In November 1939, when the war was two months old, I told the Shell Company that I wanted to join up and help in the fight against Bwana Hitler, and they released me with their blessing. In a wonderfully magnanimous gesture, they told me that they would continue to pay my salary into the bank wherever I might happen to be in the world and for as long as the war lasted and I remained alive. I thanked them very much indeed and got into my ancient little Ford Prefect and set off on the 600-mile journey from Dar es Salaam to Nairobi to enlist in the RAF.

When one is quite alone on a lengthy and slightly hazardous journey like this, every sensation of pleasure and fear is enormously intensified, and several incidents from that strange two-day safari up through central Africa in my little black Ford have remained clear in my memory.

A frequent and always wonderful sight was the astonishing number of giraffe that I passed on the first day. They were usually in groups of three or four, often with a baby alongside, and they never ceased to enthral me. They were surprisingly tame. I would see them ahead of me nibbling green leaves from the tops of acacia trees by the side of the road, and whenever I came upon them I would stop the car and get out and walk slowly towards them, shouting inane but cheery greetings up into the sky where their small heads were waving about on their long long necks. I often amazed myself by the way I behaved when I was certain that there were no other human beings within fifty miles. All my inhibitions would disappear and I would shout, 'Hello, giraffes! Hello! Hello! Hello! How are you today?' And the giraffes would incline their heads very slightly and stare down at me with languorous demure expressions, but they never ran away. I found it exhilarating to be able to walk freely among such huge graceful wild creatures and talk to them as I wished.

The road northwards through Tanganyika was narrow and often deeply rutted, and once I saw a very large thick greenish-brown cobra gliding slowly over the ruts in the road about thirty yards ahead of me. It was seven or eight feet long and was holding its flat spoon-shaped head six inches up in the air and well clear of the dusty road. I stopped the car smartly so as not to run it over, and to be truthful I was so frightened I went quickly into reverse and kept backing away until the fearsome thing had disappeared into the undergrowth. I never lost my fear of snakes all the time I was in the tropics. They gave me the shivers.

At the Wami river the natives put my car on a raft and six strong men on the opposite bank started to pull me across the hundred yards or so of water with a rope, chanting as they pulled. The river was running swiftly and in midstream the slim raft upon which my car and I were balanced began to get carried down-river by the current. The six strong men chanted louder and pulled harder and I sat helpless in the car watching the crocodiles swimming around the raft, and the crocodiles stared

ferry at Wami River

up at me with their cruel black eyes. I was bobbing about on that river for over an hour, but in the end the six strong men won their battle with the currents and pulled me across. 'That will be three shillings, bwana,' they said, laughing.

Only once did I see any elephant. I saw a big tusker and his cow and their one baby moving slowly forward in line astern about fifty yards from the road on the edge of the forest. I stopped the car to watch them but I did not get out. The elephants never saw me and I was able to stay gazing at them for quite a while. A great sense of peace and serenity seemed to surround these massive, slow-moving, gentle beasts. Their skin hung loose over their bodies like suits they had inherited from larger ancestors, with the trousers ridiculously baggy. Like the giraffes they were vegetarians and did not have to hunt or kill in order to survive in the jungle, and no other wild beast would ever dare to threaten them. Only the foul humans in the shape of an occasional big-game hunter or an ivory poacher were to be feared, but this small elephant family did not look as though they had yet met any of these horrors. They seemed to be leading a life of absolute contentment. They are better off than me, I told myself, and a good deal wiser. I myself am at this moment on my way to kill Germans or to be killed by them, but those elephants have no thought of murder in their minds.

At the frontier between Tanganyika and Kenya there was a wooden gate across the road with an old shack alongside it, and in command of this great outpost of Customs and Immigration was an ancient and toothless black man who told me he had been there for thirty-seven years. He gave me a cup of tea and said he was sorry he did not have any sugar to put into it. I asked him if he wished to see my passport but he shook his head and said all passports looked the same to him. In any event, he added, smiling secretly, he could not read without spectacles and he did not possess any.

Outside the Customs shack, a group of enormous Masai tribesmen holding spears were crowding round my car. They stared at me curiously and patted the car with their hands, but we were unable to understand each other's language.

A little later on, I was bumping along on a particularly

narrow bit of road through some very thick jungle when all of a sudden the sun went down and in ten minutes darkness descended over the jungle land. My headlamps were very dim. It would have been foolish to push on through the night. So I parked just off the road in a scrubby patch of thorn trees to wait for the dawn, and I sat in the car with the window down and poured myself a tot of whisky with water. I drank it slowly, listening to the jungle noises all around me and I was not afraid. A car is good protection against almost any wild animal. I had with me a sandwich with hard cheese inside it and I ate that with my whisky. Then I wound up the two windows, leaving just a half-inch gap at the top of each, and got into the back seat and curled up and went to sleep.

Flying Training, Nairobi

I reached Nairobi at about three o'clock the next afternoon and drove straight to the aerodrome where the small RAF headquarters was situated. There I was given a medical examination by an affable English doctor who remarked that six feet six inches was not the ideal height for a flier of aeroplanes.

'Does that mean you can't pass me for flying duties?' I asked him fearfully.

'Funnily enough,' he said, 'there is no mention of a height limit in my instructions, so I can pass you with a clear conscience. Good luck, my boy.'

I was fitted out with a simple uniform which consisted of khaki shorts and shirt and jacket and khaki stockings and black shoes, and I was given the rank of Leading Aircraftman (LAC) which is one below a Corporal. Then I was led over to a Nissen hut where my fellow trainees were already installed. There were sixteen of us altogether learning to fly in this Initial Training School in Nairobi, and I liked every one of my companions. They were all young men like me who had come out from England to work for some large commercial concern, usually either Barclays Bank or Imperial Tobacco, and who had now volunteered for flying duties. We were to spend the next six months training together in very close association, and then we would all be separated and posted off to various operational squadrons. It is a fact, and I verified it carefully later, that out of those sixteen, no fewer than thirteen were killed in the air within the next two years.

In retrospect, one gasps at the waste of life.

At the aerodrome we had three instructors and three planes. The instructors were civil airline pilots borrowed by the RAF from a small domestic company called Wilson Airways. The planes were Tiger Moths. The Tiger Moth is or was a thing of great beauty. Everybody who has ever flown a Tiger Moth has fallen in love with it. It is a totally efficient and very aerobatic little biplane powered by a Gypsy engine, and as my instructor told me, a Gypsy engine has never been known to fail in mid-air. You could throw a Tiger Moth about all over the sky and nothing ever broke. You could glide it upside down hanging in your straps for minutes on end, and although the engine cut out when you did that because the carburettor was also upside down, the motor started again at once when you turned her the right way up again. You could spin her vertically downwards for thousands of feet and then all she needed was a touch on the rudder-bar, a bit of throttle and the stick pushed forward and out she came in a couple of flips. A Tiger Moth had no vices. She never dropped a wing if you lost flying speed coming in to land, and she would suffer innumerable heavy landings from incompetent beginners without turning a hair. There were two cockpits in a Tiger Moth, one for the instructor and one for the pupil, and you could talk to each other while in flight through a rubber mouthpiece. She had no refinements and of course no self-starter, so that the only way to start the engine was to stand in front and swing the propeller by hand. When you did this, you took great care not to lose your balance and fall forward otherwise the prop would chop off your head.

Nairobi
4 December 1939

Dear Mama,

I'm having a lovely time, have never enjoyed myself so much. I've been sworn in to the R. A. F. proper and am definitely in it now until the end of the war. My rank – a Leading Aircraftman, with every opportunity of becoming a pilot officer in a few months if I don't make a B.F. of myself. No boys to do everything for me anymore. Get your own food, wash your own knives and forks, fold up your own clothes, and in short, do everything for yourself. I suppose I'd better not say too much about what we do or when we are going because the letter would probably be torn up by the censor, but we wake at 5.30 a.m., drill before breakfast till 7 a.m., fly and attend lectures till 12.30. 12.30/1.30 lunch – 1.30 to 6.00 p.m. flying and lectures. The flying is grand and our instructors are extremely pleasant and proficient. With any luck I'll be flying solo by the end of this week . . .

There was only one runway on the little Nairobi aerodrome and this gave everyone plenty of practice at cross-wind landings and take-offs. And on most mornings, before flying began, we all had to run out on to the airfield and chase the zebras away.

When flying a military aeroplane, you sit on your parachute, which adds another six inches to your height. When I got into the open cockpit of a Tiger Moth for the first time and sat down on my parachute, my entire head stuck up in the open air. The engine was running and I was getting a rush of wind full in the face from the slipstream.

'You are too tall,' the instructor whose name was

Flying Officer Parkinson said. 'Are you sure you want to do this?'

'Yes please,' I said.

'Wait till we rev her up for take-off,' Parkinson said. 'You'll have a job to breathe. And keep those goggles down or you'll be blinded by watering eyes.'

Parkinson was right. On the first flight I was almost asphyxiated by the slipstream and survived only by ducking down into the cockpit for deep breaths every few seconds. After that, I tied a thin cotton scarf around my nose and mouth and this made breathing possible.

I see from my Log Book, which I still have, that I went solo after 7 hours 40 minutes, which was about average. An RAF pilot's Log Book, by the way, is, or certainly was in those days, quite a formidable affair. It was an almost square (8" × 9") book, 1" thick and bound between two very hard covers faced with blue canvas. You never lost your Log Book. It contained a record of every flight you had ever made as well as the plane you were flying, the purpose and destination of the trip and the time you had spent in the air.

After I had gone solo, I was allowed to go up alone for much of the time and it was wonderful. How many young men, I kept asking myself, were lucky enough to be allowed to go whizzing and soaring through the sky above a country as beautiful as Kenya? Even the aeroplane and the petrol were free! In the Great Rift Valley the big game and smaller game were as plentiful as cows on a dairy farm, and I flew low in my little Tiger Moth to look at them. Oh, the animals I saw every day from that cockpit! I would fly for long periods at a height of no more than

YEAR 1939		AIRCRAFT		PILOT, OR 1ST PILOT	2ND PILOT, PUPIL OR PASSENGER	DUTY (INCLUDING RESULTS AND REMARKS)
MONTH	DATE	Type	No.			
						NAIROBI
						— TOTALS BROUGHT FORWARD
Jan.	27	TIGER	K36	F/O MARKHAM	SELF	OBSERVATION FLIGHT.
"	28	TIGER	K36	F/O MARKHAM	SELF	AERIAL FLYING - AIR TURNS.
"	28	TIGER	K20	F/O MARKHAM	SELF	AIR TURNS - TAKE OFFS.
"	29	TIGER	K36	F/O MARKHAM	SELF	TAKE OFFS, FLYING, STALLS.
"	30	TIGER	K36	F/O MARKHAM	SELF	TAKE OFFS, LANDING, APPROACH. N.
"	31	TIGER	K36	F/O MARKHAM	SELF	TAKE OFFS, STEEP TURN, LANDING.
DEC 1	3	TIGER	K36	F/O MARKHAM	SELF	TAKE OFFS, LANDINGS
"	4	TIGER	K36	F/O MARKHAM	SELF	TAKE OFF, LANDINGS
"	5	TIGER	K36	F/O MARKHAM	SELF	LANDINGS
"	5	TIGER	K36	F/O MARKHAM	SELF	LANDINGS
"	6	TIGER	K36	F/O MARKHAM	SELF	LANDINGS
"	7	TIGER	K36	F/O MARKHAM	SELF	LANDINGS
"	7	TIGER	K36	F/O MARKHAM	SELF	LANDINGS
"	8	TIGER	K36	F/O MARKHAM	SELF	LANDINGS
"	9	TIGER	K36	F/O MARKHAM	SELF	LANDINGS
"	11	TIGER	K36	F/O MARKHAM	SELF	LANDINGS
"	12	TIGER	K36	F/O MARKHAM	SELF	LANDINGS
"	12	TIGER	K36	F/O MARKHAM	SELF	LANDINGS
"	13	TIGER	K36	F/O MARKHAM	SELF	LANDINGS
"	13	TIGER	K28	SELF		(FIRST SOLO)
"	14	TIGER	K28	F/O MARKHAM	SELF	LANDINGS

GRAND TOTAL [Cols. (1) to (10)] **12** Hrs **55** Mins ... TOTALS CARRIED FORWARD

CERTIFIED that I fully understand the fuel and ignition systems of the .... aircraft and the action to be taken in the event of fire.

.... Pupil.

CERTIFIED that I have been instructed in Airscrew Swinging in accordance with the standard procedure as laid down in A.P.129 (F.T.N. Part I - Chap.II paras 41 and 47)

.... Pupil.

		SINGLE ENGINE AIRCRAFT				
		DAY		NIGHT		PASS
		DUAL	PILOT	DUAL	PILOT	
		1020				
		1020				
		1020				
		1050				
		1035				
		1040				
		1035				
		2040				
		1040				
		1040				
		1040				
		1040				
		1015				
		1035				
		1035				
		1040				
		1035				
		1040				
				1035		
		1010				
		1250	0245			

sixty or seventy feet, gazing down at huge herds of buffalo and wildebeest which would stampede in all directions as I whizzed over. From an illustrated book I had bought in Nairobi, I learnt to recognize kudu, Thomson's gazelle, eland, impala and many other animals. I saw plenty of giraffe and rhino and elephant and lion, and once I spotted a leopard, sleek as silk, lying along the trunk of a large tree. He was watching some impala grazing below him and deciding which one to have for his dinner. I flew over the pink flamingos on Lake Nakuru and I flew all the way round the snow summit of Mount Kenya in my trusty little Tiger Moth. What a fortunate fellow I am, I kept telling myself. Nobody has ever had such a lovely time as this!

The initial training took eight weeks, and at the end of it we were all fairly competent fliers of light single-engined aircraft. We could loop the loop and fly upside down. We could get ourselves out of a spin. We could do forced landings with the engine cut. We could side-slip and land decently in a strong cross-wind. We could navigate our way solo from Nairobi to Eldoret or Nakuru and back with plenty of cloud about, and we were full of confidence.

As soon as we had passed out of Initial Training School in Nairobi, we were put on a train bound for Kampala, in Uganda. The journey took a day and a night, and the train was so slow that we spent a lot of the time, frisky youngbloods that we were, climbing up on to the roofs of the carriages and running the whole length of the train and back, jumping over the gaps between the carriages.

At Kampala there was an Imperial Airways flying-boat moored on the lake and waiting to take the sixteen of us

2,000 miles north, to Cairo. By now we were half-trained pilots and wherever we went we were treated as moderately valuable properties. We ourselves were bursting with energy and exuberance and perhaps a touch of self-importance as well because now we were intrepid flying men and devils of the sky.

Nairobi
18 December 1939

Dear Mama,

Well, everything here is also going very smoothly. I did my first solo flight some days ago and now go up alone for longish periods every day. I've just learnt to loop the loop and spin and the next thing we've got to do is flying upside down, which isn't quite so funny. But it's all marvellous fun . . .

LAC Ballantyne, me, Fabian Wallis

The great flying-boat flew low for the whole of the long journey, and as we passed over the wild and barren lands where Kenya meets the Sudan we saw literally hundreds of elephant. They seemed to move around in herds of about twenty, always with a mighty bull tusker leading the herd and with the cows and their babies in the rear. Never, I kept reminding myself as I peered down through the small round window of the flying-boat, never will I see anything like this again.

Soon we found the upper reaches of the Nile and followed it down to Wadi Halfa, where we landed to refuel. Wadi Halfa then was one corrugated-iron shed with a lot of 44-gallon drums of petrol lying around, and the river was narrow and very fast. We all marvelled at the skill of the pilot as he put the great lumbering flying-machine down on that rushing strip of water.

In Cairo we landed on a very different Nile, wide and sluggish, and we were shuttled ashore and taken to Heliopolis aerodrome and put on board a monstrous and ancient transport plane whose wings were joined together with bits of wire.

'Where are they taking us to?' we asked.

'To Iraq,' they answered, 'and jolly good luck to you all.'

'What do you mean by that?'

'We mean that you are going to Habbaniya in Iraq and Habbaniya is the most godforsaken hell-hole in the entire world,' they said, smirking. 'It is where you will stay for six months to complete your advanced flying training, after which you will be ready to join a squadron and face the enemy.'

Habbaniya
20 February 1940

Dear Mama,

   *Here is a not very good photo taken of me in the streets of
Cairo by one of those men who pop up from behind a public
lavatory and snap you and hand you a bit of paper telling you to
call tomorrow for the print . . .*

Unless you had been there and seen it with your own eyes you could not believe that a place like Habbaniya existed. It was a vast assemblage of hangars and Nissen huts and brick bungalows set slap in the middle of a boiling desert on the banks of the muddy Euphrates river miles from anywhere. The nearest place to it was Baghdad, about 100 miles to the north.

This amazing and nonsensical RAF outpost was colossal. It was at least a mile long on each of its four sides, and there were paved streets called Bond Street

"Filthy" Leuchars, me.—Habbaniya

and Regent Street and Tottenham Court Road. There were hospitals and dental surgeries and canteens and recreation halls and I don't know how many thousands of men lived there. What they did I never discovered. It was beyond me why anyone should want to build a vast RAF town in such an abominable, unhealthy, desolate place as Habbaniya.

> *Habbaniya*
> *10 July 1940*
>
> *Dear Mama,*
>   *We've been here nearly 5 months now, and as we get nearer and nearer to the time when our course is finished and we go elsewhere we get more and more thrilled. It will be curious to see ordinary men and actual women doing ordinary things in ordinary places once more, to call a taxi or use the telephone; to order what you want to eat or to see a train; to go up a flight of stairs or see a row of houses. All these things and many more I shall derive the very greatest pleasure from doing . . .*

At Habbaniya we flew from dawn until 11 a.m. After that, as the temperature in the shade moved up towards 115°F, everyone had to stay indoors until it cooled down again. We were flying more powerful planes now, Hawker Harts with Rolls-Royce Merlin engines, and everything became suddenly much more serious. The Harts had machine-guns on their wings and we would practise shooting down the enemy by firing at a canvas drogue towed behind another plane.

My Log Book tells me that we were at Habbaniya from

20 February 1940 to 20 August 1940, for exactly six months, and apart from the flying which was always exhilarating, it was a pretty tedious period of my young life. There were minor excitements now and then to relieve the boredom such as the flooding of the Euphrates when we had to evacuate the entire camp to a windswept plateau for ten days. People got stung by scorpions and went into hospital for a while to recover. The Iraqi tribesmen sometimes took pot shots at us from the surrounding hills. Men occasionally got heatstroke and had to be packed in ice. Everyone suffered from prickly heat and itched all over for much of the time.

But eventually we got our wings and were judged ready to move on and confront the real enemy. About one half of the sixteen of us were given commissions and promoted to the rank of Pilot Officer. The other half were made Sergeant Pilots, though how this rather arbitrary class-conscious division was made I never knew. We were also divided up into fighter pilots or bomber pilots, fliers either of single-engined planes or twins. I became a Pilot Officer and a fighter pilot. Then all sixteen of us said goodbye to one another and were whisked off in many different directions.

I found myself at a large RAF station on the Suez Canal called Ismailia, where they told me that I had been posted to 80 Squadron who were flying Gladiators against the Italians in the Western Desert of Libya. The Gloster Gladiator was an out-of-date fighter biplane with a radial engine. Back in England at that time, all the fighter boys were flying Hurricanes and Spitfires, but they were not

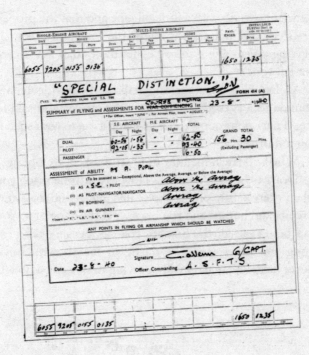

sending any of those little beauties out to us in the Middle East quite yet.

The Gladiator was armed with two fixed machine-guns, and these actually fired bullets *through* the revolving propeller. To me, this was about the greatest piece of magic I had ever seen in my life. I simply could not understand how two machine-guns firing thousands of bullets a minute could be synchronized to fire their bullets *through* a propeller revolving at thousands of revs a minute without hitting the propeller blades. I was told it had something to do with a little oil pipe and that the propeller shaft communicated with the machine-guns by sending pulses along the pipe, but more than that I cannot tell you.

At Ismailia, a rather supercilious Flight-Lieutenant pointed to a parked Gladiator on the tarmac and said to me, 'That one's yours. You'll be flying it out to your squadron tomorrow.'

'Who will teach me how to fly it?' I asked, trembling.

'Don't be an ass,' he said. 'How can anyone teach you when there's only one cockpit? Just get in and do a few circuits and bumps and you'll soon get the hang of it. You had better get all the practice you can because the next thing you know you'll be dicing in the air with some clever little Italian who will be trying to shoot you down.'

I remember thinking at the time that this was surely not the right way of doing things. They had spent eight months and a great deal of money training me to fly and suddenly that was the end of it all. Nobody in Ismailia was going to teach me anything about air-to-air combat, and they were certainly not going to take time off to instruct me when I joined a busy operational squadron. There is no question that we were flung in at the deep end, totally unprepared for actual fighting in the air, and this, in my opinion, accounted for the very great losses of young pilots that we suffered out there. I myself survived only by the skin of my teeth.

Survival

Some forty years ago I described in a story called 'A Piece of Cake' what it was like to find myself strapped firmly into the cockpit of my Gladiator with a fractured skull and a bashed-in face and a fuzzy mind while the crashed plane was going up in flames on the sands of the Western Desert. But there is an aspect of that story that I feel ought to be clarified by me and it is this. There seems, on re-reading it, to be an implication that I was shot down by enemy action, and if I remember rightly, this was inserted by the editors of an American magazine called the *Saturday Evening Post* who originally bought and published it. Those were the war years and the more dramatic the story, the better it was. They actually called it 'Shot Down in Libya', so you can see what they were getting at. The fact is that my crash had nothing whatsoever to do with enemy action. I was not shot down either by another plane or from the ground. Here is what happened.

I had climbed into my new Gladiator at an RAF airfield called Abu Suweir on the Suez Canal, and had set off alone to join 80 Squadron in the Western Desert. This was going to be my very first venture into combat territory. The date was 19 September 1940. They told me to fly across the Nile delta and land at a small airfield called Amiriya, near Alexandria, to refuel. Then I should fly on and land again at a bomber airfield in Libya called Fouka

The Eastern Mediterranean

for a second refuelling. At Fouka I was to report to the Commanding Officer who would tell me precisely where 80 Squadron were at that moment, and I would then fly on and join them. A forward airfield in the Western Desert was in those days never much more than a strip of sand surrounded by tents and parked aircraft, and these airfields were being moved very frequently from one site to another, depending on whether the front line of the army was advancing or retreating.

The flight in itself was a fairly daunting one for someone who had virtually no experience of the aircraft he was flying and none at all of flying long distances over Egypt and Libya with no navigational aids to help him. I had no radio. All I had was a map strapped to one knee. It took me one hour exactly to get from Abu Suweir to Amiriya where I landed with some difficulty in a sandstorm. But I got my plane refuelled and set off as quickly as I could for Fouka. I landed at Fouka fifty-five minutes later (all these times are meticulously recorded in my Log Book) and reported to the CO in his tent. He made some calls on his field telephone and then asked me for my map.

'Eighty Squadron are now there,' he said, pointing to a spot in the middle of the desert about thirty miles due south of the small coastal town of Mersah Matrûh.

'Will it be easy to see?' I asked him.

'You can't miss it,' he said. 'You'll see the tents and about fifteen Gladiators parked around the place. You can spot it from miles away.' I thanked him and went off to calculate my course and distance.

The time was 6.15 p.m. when I took off from Fouka for

80 Squadron's landing strip. I estimated my flight time to be fifty minutes at the most. That would give me fifteen or twenty minutes to spare before darkness fell, which should be ample.

I flew straight for the point where the 80 Squadron airfield should have been. It wasn't there. I flew around the area to the north, south, east and west, but there was not a sign of an airfield. Below me there was nothing but empty desert, and rather rugged desert at that, full of large stones and boulders and gullies.

At this point, dusk began to fall and I realized that I was in trouble. My fuel was running low and there was no way I could get back to Fouka on what I had left. I couldn't have found it in the dark anyway. The only course open to me now was to make a forced landing in the desert and make it quickly, before it was too dark to see.

I skimmed low over the boulder-strewn desert searching for just one small strip of reasonably flat sand on which to land. I knew the direction of the wind so I knew precisely the direction that my approach should take. But where, oh where was there one little patch of desert that was clear of boulders and gullies and lumps of rock. There simply wasn't one. It was nearly dark now. I *had* to get down somehow or other. I chose a piece of ground that seemed to me to be as boulder-free as any and I made an approach. I came in as slowly as I dared, hanging on the prop, travelling just above my stalling speed of eighty miles an hour. My wheels touched down. I throttled back and prayed for a bit of luck.

I didn't get it. My undercarriage hit a boulder and

collapsed completely and the Gladiator buried its nose in the sand at what must have been about seventy-five miles an hour.

My injuries in that bust-up came from my head being thrown forward violently against the reflector-sight when the plane hit the ground (in spite of the fact that I was strapped tightly, as always, into the cockpit), and apart from the skull fracture, the blow pushed my nose in and knocked out a few teeth and blinded me completely for days to come.

It is odd that I can remember very clearly quite a few of the things that followed seconds after the crash. Obviously I was unconscious for some moments, but I must have recovered my senses very quickly because I can remember hearing a mighty *whoosh* as the petrol tank in the port wing exploded, followed almost at once by another mighty *whoosh* as the starboard tank went up in flames. I could see nothing at all, and I felt no pain. All I wanted was to go gently off to sleep and to hell with the flames. But soon a tremendous heat around my legs galvanized my soggy brain into action. With great difficulty I managed to undo first my seat-straps and then the straps of my parachute, and I can even remember the desperate effort it took to push myself upright in the cockpit and roll out head first on to the sand below. Again I wanted to lie down and doze off, but the heat close by was terrific and had I stayed where I was I should simply have been roasted alive. I began very very slowly to drag myself away from the awful hotness. I heard my machine-gun ammunition exploding in the flames and the bullets were pinging about all over the place but that didn't worry me. All I wanted was to get away from the tremendous heat and rest in peace. The world about me was divided sharply down the middle into two halves. Both of these halves were pitch black, but one was scorching-hot and the other was not. I had to keep on dragging myself away from the scorching-hot side and into the cooler one, and this took a long time and enormous effort, but in the end the temperature all around me became bearable. When that happened I collapsed and went to sleep.

It was revealed at an inquiry into my crash held later that the CO at Fouka had given me totally wrong information. Eighty Squadron had never been in the position I was sent to. They were fifty miles to the south, and the place to which I had been sent was actually no-man's-land, which was a strip of sand in the Western Desert about half a mile wide dividing the front lines of the British and Italian armies. I am told that the flames from my burning aircraft lit up the sand dunes for miles around, and of course not only the crash but also the subsequent bonfire were witnessed by the soldiers of both sides. The watchers in the trenches had been observing my antics for some time, and both sides knew that it was an RAF fighter and not an Italian plane that had come down. The remains, if any, were therefore of more interest to our people than to the enemy.

When the flames had died down and the desert was dark, a little patrol of three brave men from the Suffolk Regiment crawled out from the British lines to inspect the wreck. They did not think for one moment that they

Logbook:

YEAR 1940	AIRCRAFT		PILOT, OR 1ST PILOT	2ND PILOT, PUPIL OR PASSENGER	DUTY (INCLUDING RESULTS AND REMARKS)
Month / Date	Type	No.			
					Totals Brought Forward
Sept. 19	GLADIATOR	—	SELF	—	Abu Sueir to Amriya
" 19	GLADIATOR	—		—	Amriya to Fouka
" 19	GLADIATOR	—		—	Fouka To 80 Sqdn
					(crashed South of
					Zero Zelten —
					Machine burned)
					6 months Hospital — 4 Mf (flying)

Telegram:

CABLE AND WIRELESS
LIMITED

E3I678

"Via Imperial"

OFFICE OF ISSUE

ALEXANDRIA

FWXA93H ALX 43 8 1410

NLT DAHL WOODLANDS FARM =

MANY HAPPY RETURNS AND LOVE CRASHED IN DESERT
TWO WEEKS AGO CAUGHT FIRE BUT ONLY CONCUSSION
BROKEN NOSE ABSOLUTELY OKAY SOON ADDRESS FOR
FEW WEEKS ANGLOSWISS HOSPITAL ALEXANDRIA DONT
EXPECT ANY LETTERS LOVE TO ALL =

ROALD DAHL

No 65 CENSOR

would find anything but a burnt-out fuselage and a charred skeleton, and they were apparently astounded when they came upon my still-breathing body lying in the sand nearby.

When they turned me over in the dark to get a better look, I must have swum back into consciousness because I can distinctly remember hearing one of them asking me how I felt, but I was unable to reply. Then I heard them whispering together about how they were going to get me back to the lines without a stretcher.

The next thing I can remember a long time later was a man's voice speaking loudly to me and telling me that he knew I was unable to see him or to answer him, but he thought there was a chance I could hear him. He told me he was an English doctor and that I was in an underground first-aid post in Mersah Matrûh. He said they were going to take me to the train by ambulance and send me back to Alexandria.

I heard him talking to me and I understood what he was saying, and I also knew all about Mersah Matrûh and about the train. Mersah was a small town about 250 miles along the Libyan coast west of Alexandria, and our army had a most carefully preserved little railway running across the desert between the two places. This railway was a vital supply line for our forward troops in the Western Desert and the Italians were bombing it all the time but we somehow managed to keep it going. Everyone knew about the single-track railway-line that ran all the way along the coast beside the sparkling white beaches of the southern Mediterranean from Alex to Mersah.

I heard voices around me as they manoeuvred my stretcher into the ambulance, and when the ambulance started to move forward over the very bumpy track, someone above me began screaming. Every time we hit a bump the man above me cried out in agony.

When they were putting me on to the train, I felt a hand on my shoulder and a lovely Cockney voice said, 'Cheer up, matey. You'll soon be back in Alex.'

The next thing I can remember was being taken off the train into the tremendous bustle of Alexandria Station, and I heard a woman's voice saying, 'This one's an officer. He'll go to the Anglo-Swiss.'

Then I was inside the hospital itself and I heard the wheels of my stretcher rumbling softly along endless corridors. 'Put him in here for the moment,' a different woman's voice was saying. 'We want to have a look at him before he goes into the ward.'

Deft fingers began to unroll the bandages around my head. 'Can you hear me talking to you?' the owner of the fingers was saying. She took one of my hands in hers and said, 'If you can hear what I am saying, just give my hand a squeeze.' I squeezed her hand. 'Good,' she said. 'That's fine. Now we know you're going to be all right.'

Then she said, 'Here he is, doctor. I've taken off the dressings. He is conscious and is responding.'

I felt the close proximity of the doctor's face as he bent over me, and I heard him saying, 'Do you have much pain?'

Now that the bandages had been taken off my head, I found myself able to burble an answer to him. 'No,' I said. 'No pain. But I can't see.'

'Don't worry about that,' the doctor said. 'All you've got to do is to lie very still. Don't move. Do you want to empty your bladder?'

'Yes,' I said.

'We'll help you,' he said, 'but don't move. Don't try to do anything for yourself.'

I believe they inserted a catheter because I felt them doing something down there and it hurt a bit, but then the pressure on my bladder went away.

'Just a dry dressing for the moment, Sister,' the doctor said. 'We'll X-ray him in the morning.'

Then I was in a ward with a lot of other men who talked and joked a good deal among themselves. I lay there dozing and feeling no pain at all, and later on the air-raid sirens started wailing and the ack-ack guns began opening up on all sides and I heard a lot of bombs exploding not very far away. I knew it was night-time now because that was when the Italian bombers came over seven nights a week to raid our navy in Alexandria harbour. I felt very calm and dreamy lying there listening to the terrific commotion of bombs and ack-ack going on outside. It was as though I had ear-phones on and all the noise was coming to me over the wireless from miles and miles away.

I knew when the morning came because the whole ward began to bustle and breakfasts were served all round. Obviously I couldn't eat because my whole head was sheathed in bandages with only small holes left for breathing. I didn't want to eat anyway. I was always sleepy. One of my arms was strapped to a board because tubes were going into the arm, but the other, the right arm, was free and once I explored the bandages on my head with my fingers. Then the Sister was saying to me, 'We are moving your bed into another room where it is quieter and you can be by yourself.'

So they wheeled me out of the ward into a single room, and over the next one or two or three days, I don't know how many, I submitted in a semi-daze to various procedures such as X-rays and being taken several times to the operating theatre. One of my more vivid recollections is of a conversation that went on in the theatre itself between a doctor and me. I knew I was in the theatre because they always told me where they were taking me, and this time the doctor said to me, 'Well, young man, we are going to use a super brand-new anaesthetic on you today. It's just come out from England and it is given by injection.' I had had short talks with this particular doctor several times. He was an anaesthetist and had visited me in my room before each operation to put his stethoscope on my chest and back. All my life I have taken an intense and inquisitive interest in every form of medicine, and even in those young days I had begun to ask the doctors a lot of questions. This man, perhaps because I was blind, always took the trouble to treat me as an intelligent listener.

'What is it called?' I asked him.

'Sodium pentathol,' he answered.

'And you have never used it before?'

'I have never used it myself,' he said, 'but it has been a great success back home as a pre-anaesthetic. It is very quick and comfortable.'

I could sense that there were quite a few other people,

men and women, padding silently around the operating theatre in their rubber boots and I could hear the tinkling of instruments lifted and put down, and the talk of soft voices. Both my senses of smell and of hearing had become very acute since my blindness, and I had developed an instinctive habit of translating sounds and scents into a coloured mental picture. I was picturing the operating theatre now, so white and sterile with the masked and green-gowned inmates going priestlike about their separate tasks, and I wondered where the surgeon was, the great man who was going to do all the cutting and the stitching.

I was about to have a major operation performed on my face, and the man who was doing it had been a famous Harley Street plastic surgeon before the war, but now he was a Surgeon-Commander in the navy. One of the nurses had told me about his Harley Street days that morning. 'You'll be all right with him,' she had said. 'He's a wonder-worker. And it's all free. A job like you're having would be costing you five hundred guineas in civvy street.'

'You mean this is the very first time you've ever used this anaesthetic?' I said to the anaesthetist.

This time he didn't answer me directly. 'You'll love it,' he said. 'You go out like a light. You don't even have any sensation of losing consciousness as you do with all the others. So here we go. You'll just feel a little prick on the back of your hand.'

I felt the needle going into a vein on the top of my left hand and I lay there waiting for the moment when I would 'go out like a light'.

I was quite unafraid. I have never been frightened by surgeons or of being given an anaesthetic, and to this day, after some sixteen major operations on numerous parts of my body, I still have complete faith in all, or let me say *nearly* all, those men of medicine.

I lay there waiting and waiting and absolutely nothing happened. My bandages had been taken off for the operation, but my eyes were still permanently closed by the swellings on my face. One doctor had told me it was quite possible that my eyes had not been damaged at all. I doubted that myself. It seemed to me that I had been permanently blinded, and as I lay there in my quiet black room where all sounds, however tiny, had suddenly become twice as loud, I had plenty of time to think about what total blindness would mean in the future. Curiously enough, it did not frighten me. It did not even depress me. In a world where war was all around me and where I had ridden in dangerous little aeroplanes that roared and zoomed and crashed and caught fire, blindness, not to mention life itself, was no longer too important. Survival was not something one struggled for any more. I was already beginning to realize that the only way to conduct oneself in a situation where bombs rained down and bullets whizzed past, was to accept the dangers and all the consequences as calmly as possible. Fretting and sweating about it all was not going to help.

The doctor had tried to comfort me by saying that when you have contusions and swellings as massive as mine, you have to wait at least until the swellings go down and the incrustations of blood around the eyelids have come away. 'Give yourself a chance,' he had said. 'Wait until those eyelids are able to open again.'

Having at this moment no eyelids to open and shut, I hoped the anaesthetist wouldn't start thinking that his famous new wonder anaesthetic had put me to sleep when it hadn't. I didn't want them to start before I was ready. 'I'm still awake,' I said.

'I know you are,' he said.

'What's going on?' I heard another man's voice asking. 'Isn't it working?' This, I knew, was the surgeon, the great man from Harley Street.

'It doesn't seem to be having any effect at all,' the anaesthetist said.

'Give him some more.'

'I have, I have,' the anaesthetist answered, and I thought I detected a slightly ruffled edge to the man's voice.

'London said it was the greatest discovery since chloroform,' the surgeon was saying. 'I saw the report myself. Matthews wrote it. Ten seconds, it said, and the patient's out. Simply tell him to count to ten and he's out before he gets to eight, that's what the report said.'

'This patient could have counted to a hundred,' the anaesthetist was saying.

It occurred to me that they were talking to one another as though I wasn't there. I would have been happier if they had kept quiet.

'Well, we can't wait all day,' the surgeon was saying. It was *his* turn to get irritable now. But I did not want my surgeon to be irritable when he was about to perform a delicate operation on my face. He had come into my room the day before and after examining me carefully, he had said, 'We can't have you going about like that for the rest of your life, can we?'

That worried me. It would have worried anyone. 'Like what?' I had asked him.

'I am going to give you a lovely new nose,' he had said, patting me on the shoulder. 'You want to have something nice to look at when you open your eyes again, don't you. Did you ever see Rudolph Valentino in the cinema?'

'Yes,' I said.

'I shall model your nose on his,' the surgeon said. 'What do you think of Rudolph Valentino, Sister?'

'He's smashing,' the Sister said.

And now, in the operating theatre, that same surgeon was saying to the anaesthetist, 'I'd forget that pentathol stuff if I were you. We really can't wait any longer. I've got four more on my list this morning.'

'Right!' snapped the anaesthetist. 'Bring me the nitrous oxide.'

I felt the rubber mask being put over my nose and mouth, and soon the blood-red circles began going round and round faster and faster like a series of gigantic scarlet flywheels and then there was an explosion and I knew nothing more.

When I regained consciousness I was back in my room. I lay there for an uncounted number of weeks but you must not think that I was totally without company during that time. Every morning throughout those black and sightless days a nurse, always the same one, would come into my room and bathe my eyes with something soft and wet. She was very gentle and very careful and she never hurt me. For at least an hour she would sit on my bed working skilfully on my swollen sealed-up eyes, and she would talk to me while she worked. She told me that the Anglo-Swiss used to be a large civilian hospital and that when war broke out the navy took over the whole place. All the doctors and all the nurses in the hospital were navy people, she said.

'Are you in the navy?' I asked her.

'Yes,' she said. 'I am a naval officer.'

'Why am *I* here if it's all navy?'

'We're taking in the RAF and the army as well now,' she said. 'That's where most of the casualties are coming from.'

Her name, she told me, was Mary Welland, and her home was in Plymouth. Her father was a Commander on a cruiser operating somewhere in the north Atlantic, and her mother worked with the Red Cross in Plymouth. She said with a smile in her voice that it was very bad form for a nurse to sit on a patient's bed, but what she was doing to my eyes was very delicate work that could only be done if she were sitting close to me. She had a lovely soft voice, and I began to picture to myself the face that went with the voice, the delicate features, the green-blue eyes, the golden-brown hair and the pale skin. Sometimes, as she worked very close to my eyes, I would feel her warm and faintly marmalade breath on my cheek and in no time at all I began to fall very quickly and quite dizzily in love with Mary Welland's invisible image. Every morning, I waited impatiently for the door to open and for the tinkling sound of the trolley as she wheeled it into my room.

Her features, I decided, were very much like those of Myrna Loy. Myrna Loy was a Hollywood cinema actress I had seen many times on the silver screen, and up until then she had been my idea of the perfect beauty. But now I took Miss Loy's face and made it even more beautiful and gave it to Mary Welland. The only concrete thing I had to go by was the voice, and so far as I was concerned, Mary Welland's dulcet tones were infinitely preferable to Myrna Loy's harsh American twang.

For about an hour every day I experienced ecstasy as Miss Myrna Mary Loy Welland sat on my bed and did things to my face and eyes with her delicate fingers. And then suddenly, I don't know how many days later, came the moment that I can never forget.

Mary Welland was working away on my right eye with one of her soft moist pads when all at once the eyelid began to open. At first it opened only an infinitesimal crack, but even so, a shaft of brilliant light pierced the darkness in my head and I saw before me very close . . . I saw three separate things . . . and all of them were glistening with scarlet and gold!

'I can see!' I cried. 'I can see something!'

'You can?' she said excitedly. 'Are you sure?'

'Yes! I can see something very close to me! I can see three separate things right in front of me! And nurse . . . they are all shining with red and gold! What are they, nurse? What am I seeing?'

'Try to keep calm,' she said. 'Stop jumping up and down. It's not good for you.'

'But nurse, I really can see something! Don't you believe me?'

'Is this what you are seeing?' she asked me, and now part of a hand and a pointing finger came into my line of sight. 'Is it this? Is it these?' she said, and her finger pointed at the three beautiful things of many colours that lay there shimmering against a background of purest white.

'Yes!' I cried. 'It's those! There are three of them! I can see them all! And I can see your finger!'

When many days of blackness and doubt are pierced suddenly by shining images of red and gold, the pleasure that floods into your mind is overwhelming. I lay propped up on my pillows gazing through the tiny crack in one eye at these amazing sights and wondering whether I wasn't perhaps catching a glimpse of paradise. 'What am I looking at?' I asked her.

'You are looking at a bit of my white uniform,' Mary Welland said. 'It's the bit that goes across my front, and the coloured things you can see in the middle of it make up the emblem of the Royal Naval Nursing Service. It is pinned to the left side of my bosom and it is worn by all nurses in the Royal Navy.'

Alexandria
20 November 1940

Dear Mama,

I sent you a telegram yesterday saying that I'd got up for 2 hours & had a bath – so you'll see I'm making good progress.
I arrived here about 8½ weeks ago, and was lying on my back for 7

weeks doing nothing, then sat up gradually, and now I am walking about a bit. When I came in I was a bit of a mess. My eyes didn't open (although I was always quite concious). They thought I had a fractured base (skull), but I think the Xray showed I didn't. My nose was bashed in, but they've got the most marvellous Harley Street specialists out here who've joined up for the war as Majors, and the ear nose & throat man pulled my nose out of the back of my head, and shaped it and now it looks just as before except that its a little bent about. That was of course under a general anesthetic.

My eyes still ache if I read or write much, but they say that they think they'll get back to normal again, and that I'll be fit for flying in about 3 months. In between I still have about 6 or more weeks sick leave here in Alex when I get out, doing nothing in a marvellous sunny climate, just like an English Summer, except that the sun shines every day.

I suppose you want to know how I crashed. Well, I'm not allowed to give you any details of what I was doing or how it happened. But it occurred in the night not very far from the Italian front lines. The plane was on fire and after it hit the ground I was just sufficiently concious to crawl out in time, having undone my straps, and roll on the ground to put out the fire on my overalls which were alight. I wasn't burnt much, but was bleeding rather badly from the head. Anyway I lay there and waited for the ammunition which was left in my guns to go off. One after the other, well over 1000 rounds exploded and the bullets whistled about seeming to hit everything but me.

I've never fainted yet, and I think it was this tendency to remain concious which saved me from being roasted.

Anyway luckily one of our forward patrols saw the blaze, and after some time arrived and picked me up & after much ado I arrived at Mersa Matruh, (you'll see it on the map – on the coast, East of Libya). There I heard a doctor say, 'Oh, he's an Italian is he' (my white flying overalls weren't very recognizable). I told him not to be a B.F., and he gave me some morphia. In about 24 hours time I arrived where I am now, living in great luxury with lots of very nice English nursing sisters to look after me . . .

P.S. The air raids here don't worry us. The Italians are very bad bombaimers.

'But they are so *beautiful*!' I cried, staring at the emblem. There were three separate parts to it, all of them heavily embossed in raised embroidery. On top there was a golden crown with scarlet in the centre and small bits of green near its base. In the middle, below the crown, there was a gold anchor with a scarlet rope twined around it. And below the anchor there was a golden circle with a big red cross in the middle. These images and their brilliant colours have been engraved on my memory ever since.

'Keep still,' Mary Welland said. 'I think we can open this eyelid a bit more.'

I kept still and waited, and a few minutes later she succeeded in getting the eyelid wide open and I saw the whole room through that one eye. In the forefront of everything I saw Nursing Officer Welland herself sitting very close and smiling at me. 'Hello,' she said. 'Welcome back to the world.'

She was a lovely looking girl, much nicer than Myrna Loy and far more real. 'You are even more beautiful than I imagined,' I said.

'Well, thank you,' she said.

The next day she got the other eye open as well and I lay there feeling as though I was about to start my whole life over again.

Mary Welland was certainly lovely. She was gentle and kind. She remained my friend all the time I was in hospital. But there is a world of difference between falling in love with a voice and remaining in love with a person you can see. From the moment I opened my eyes, Mary became a human instead of a dream and my passion evaporated.

All the time I was in hospital, my one obsession was to get back to operational flying. The doctors told me there was virtually no hope of that. They said that even if I managed to get back perfect vision, I would still have the head injuries to contend with. Severe head injuries are not easily overcome, they said, and I had better resign myself to being shipped home eventually as a non-combatant. I admit now, although I didn't tell them at the time, that for several weeks after I had regained my sight I suffered from the most appalling headaches, but even these began gradually to grow less and less severe.

Alexandria
6 December 1940

Dear Mama,

I haven't written to you since my one and only letter some weeks ago, chiefly because the doctors said that it wasn't good for me. As a matter of fact I've been progressing very slowly. As I told you in my telegram I did start getting up, but they soon

popped me back to bed again because I got such terrific headaches.
A week ago I was moved back into this private room, and I have
just completed a whole long 7 days lying flat on my back in semi
darkness doing absolutely nothing – not even allowed to lift a
finger to wash myself. Well, that's over, and I'm sitting up today,
(its 8 o'clock in the evening actually) and writing this and
incidentally feeling fine. Tomorrow I think they are going to give
me intravenal saline and pituatory injections & make me drink
gallons of water – its another stunt to get rid of the headaches.
You needn't be alarmed – there's nothing very wrong with me, I've
merely had an extremely serious concussion. They say I certainly
won't fly for about 6 months, and last week were going to invalid
me home on the next convoy. But somehow I didn't want to – once
invalided home, I knew I'd never get on to flying again, and who
wants to be invalided home anyway. When I go I want to go
normally . . .

After four months in hospital I was allowed out of bed,
and I used to stand for hours in my dressing-gown looking out of my window at the view. The only view I had
was the courtyard of the hospital, and that wasn't much to
look at, but directly across the courtyard I could see
through a huge window into a long wide corridor. One
morning I saw a medical orderly coming down this corridor carrying a very large tray with a white cloth over it.
Walking in the opposite direction towards the orderly,
was a middle-aged woman, probably somebody from the
hospital clerical staff. When the orderly came level with
the woman, he suddenly whipped away the cloth from the
tray and pushed the tray towards the woman's face. On

the tray there lay the entire quite nakèd amputated leg of a soldier. I saw the poor woman reel backwards. I saw the foul orderly roar with laughter and replace the cloth and walk on. I saw the woman stagger to the window-sill and lean forward with her head in her hands, then she pulled herself together and went on her way. I have never forgotten that little illustration of man's repulsive behaviour towards woman.

I was finally discharged from hospital in February 1941, five months after I was admitted. I was given four weeks' convalescence which I spent in Alexandria living in total luxury in the magnificent house of a charming and very wealthy English family called Peel. Dorothy Peel was a regular hospital visitor at the Anglo-Swiss, and when she heard that I was soon to be allowed out, she said, 'Come and stay with us.' So I did, and I was a lucky fellow to have found such a splendid place among such kind people in which to gather myself together for the next round.

After four weeks with the Peels, I reported to the RAF medical examiners in Cairo, and it was a great day for me when I was once again passed fully fit for flying duties.

But where were my old squadron now?

Eighty Squadron, as it turned out, were no longer in the Western Desert. They were far across the water in Greece, where for some weeks they had been flying valiantly against the Italian invaders. But now the German armies and air forces had joined the Italians in Greece and were rapidly over-running the little country. It was obvious to everybody, even then, that the tiny token British Expeditionary Force and the handful of RAF planes in Greece were not going to be able to last long against the German juggernaut.

Where did they want me to go? I asked.

To Greece, of course, they said. They told me that 80 Squadron were no longer flying Gladiators. They were now equipped with Mark I Hurricanes. I must learn very quickly to fly a Hurricane and then I must take it to Greece and rejoin the squadron.

Convalescing, Peel's garden, Alexandria

When I got this news I was in Ismailia, a large RAF aerodrome on the Suez Canal. A Flight-Lieutenant pointed to a Hurricane standing on the tarmac and said, 'You can have a couple of days to learn how to fly it, then you take it to Greece.'

'Fly that to Greece?' I said.

'Of course.'

'Where do I stop to refuel?'

'You don't,' he said. 'You go non-stop.'

'How long will it take?'

'About four and a half hours,' he said.

Even I knew that a Hurricane had fuel for only one and a half hours' flying, and I pointed this out to the Flight-Lieutenant. 'Don't worry about that,' he said. 'We're fitting extra fuel tanks under the wings.'

'Do they work?'

'Sometimes they work,' he said, smirking. 'You press a little button and if you're lucky a pump pumps petrol from the wing-tanks into the main tank.'

'What happens if the pump doesn't work?'

'You bale out into the Med and swim,' he said.

'No,' I said. 'Be serious. Who picks me up?'

'Nobody,' he said. 'It's a chance you have to take.'

This, I told myself, is a waste of manpower and machinery. I had no experience at all in flying against the enemy. I had never been in an operational squadron. And now they wanted me to jump into a plane I had never flown before and fly it to Greece to fight against a highly efficient air force that outnumbered us by a hundred to one.

I was petrified as I strapped myself into the Hurricane

for the first time. It was the first monoplane I had ever flown. It was without a doubt the first *modern* plane I had ever flown. It was many times more powerful and speedy and tricky than anything I had ever seen. I had never flown a plane with a retractable undercarriage before. I had never flown a plane with wing-flaps which had to be used to slow down your landing speed. I had never flown a plane with a variable pitch propeller or one that had eight machine-guns in its wings. I had never flown anything like it. Somehow I managed to get the thing off the ground and back down again without smashing it up, but for me it was like riding a bucking horse. I was just beginning to learn where most of the knobs were located and what they were used for when my two days were up and I had to leave for Greece.

Ismailia
12 April 1941

Dear Mama,

A very short note to say that I'm going north across the sea almost at once to join my squadron. I telegraphed this to you today & told you where to send my letters. You may not hear much from me for quite a long while so don't worry . . .

Baling out into the Mediterranean didn't worry me nearly as much as the thought of spending four and a half hours squashed into that tiny metal cockpit. I was six feet six inches tall, and when I sat in a Hurricane I had the posture of an unborn baby in the womb, with my knees almost touching my chin. I was able to put up with that for short flights, but four and a half hours clear across the sea from Egypt to Greece was something else again. I wasn't quite sure I could do it.

I took off the next day from the bleak and sandy airfield of Abu Suweir, and after a couple of hours I was over Crete and beginning to get severe cramp in both legs. My main fuel tank was nearly empty so I pressed the little button that worked the pump to the extra tanks. The pump worked. The main tank filled up again exactly as it was meant to and on I went.

After four hours and forty minutes in the air, I landed at last on Elevsis aerodrome, near Athens, but by then I was so knotted up with terrible excruciating cramp in the legs I had to be lifted out of the cockpit by two strong men. But I had come home to my squadron at last.

First Encounter with a Bandit

So this was Greece. And what a different place from the hot and sandy Egypt I had left behind me some five hours before. Over here it was springtime and the sky a milky-blue and the air just pleasantly warm. A gentle breeze was blowing in from the sea beyond Piraeus and when I turned my head and looked inland I saw only a couple of miles away a range of massive craggy mountains as bare as bones. The aerodrome I had landed on was no more than a grassy field and wild flowers were blossoming blue and yellow and red in their millions all around me.

The two airmen who had helped to lift my cramped body out of the cockpit of the Hurricane had been most sympathetic. I leant against the wing of the plane and waited for the cramp to go out of my legs.

'A bit scrunched up in there, were you?' one of the airmen said.

'A bit,' I said. 'Yes.'

'You oughtn't to be flyin' fighters a chap of your height,' he said. 'What you want is a ruddy great bomber where you can stretch your legs out.'

'Yes,' I said. 'You're right.'

This airman was a Corporal. He had taken my parachute out of the cockpit and now he brought it over and placed it on the ground beside me. He stayed with me and it was clear that he wanted to do some more talking. 'I don't see the point of it,' he went on. 'You bring a brand-new kite, an *absolutely spanking brand-new kite* straight from the factory and you bring it all the way from ruddy Egypt to this godforsaken place and what's goin' to 'appen to it?'

'What?' I said.

'It's come even *further* than from Egypt!' he cried. 'It's come all the way from *England*, that's where it's come from! It's come all the way from England to Egypt and then all the way across the Med to this soddin' country and all for what? What's goin' to 'appen to it?'

'What *is* going to happen to it?' I asked him. I was a bit taken aback by this sudden outburst.

'I'll tell you what's goin' to 'appen to it,' the Corporal said, working himself up. 'Crash bang wallop! Shot down in flames! Explodin' in the air! Ground-strafed by the One-O-Nines right 'ere where we're standin' this very moment! Why, this kite won't last one week in this place! None of 'em do!'

'Don't say that,' I told him.

'I 'as to say it,' he said, 'because it's the truth.'

'But why such prophecies of doom?' I asked him. 'Who is going to do this to us?'

'The Krauts, of course!' he cried. 'Krauts is *pourin'* in 'ere like ruddy ants! They've got *one thousand planes* just the other side of those mountains there and what've *we* got?'

'All right then,' I said. 'What *have* we got?' I was interested to find out.

'It's pitiful what we've got,' the Corporal said.

'Tell me,' I said.

'What we've got is exactly what you can see on this

ruddy field!' he said. '*Fourteen 'urricanes*! No it isn't. It's gone up to fifteen now you've brought this one out!'

I refused to believe him. Surely it wasn't possible that fifteen Hurricanes were all we had left in the whole of Greece.

'Are you absolutely sure of this?' I asked him, aghast.

'Am I lyin'?' he said, turning to the second airman. 'Please tell this officer whether I am lyin' or whether it's the truth.'

'It's the gospel truth,' the second airman said.

'What about bombers?' I said.

'There's about four clapped-out Blenheims over there at Menidi,' the Corporal said, 'and that's the lot. *Four Blenheims and fifteen 'urricanes* is the entire ruddy RAF in the 'ole of Greece.'

'Good Lord,' I said.

'Give it another week,' he went on, 'and every one of us'll be pushed into the sea and swimmin' for 'ome!'

'I hope you're wrong.'

'There's five 'undred Kraut fighters and five 'undred Kraut bombers just around the corner,' he went on, 'and what've we got to put up against them? We've got a miserable fifteen 'urricanes and I'm mighty glad I'm not the one that's flyin' 'em! If you'd 'ad any sense at all, matey, you'd've stayed right where you were back in old Egypt.'

I could see he was nervous and I couldn't blame him. The ground-crew in a squadron, the fitters and riggers, were virtually non-combatants. They were never meant to be in the front line and because of that they were unarmed and had never been taught how to fight or defend themselves. In a situation like this, it was easier to be a pilot than one of the ground-crew. The chances of survival might be a good deal slimmer for the pilot, but he had a splendid weapon to fight with.

The Corporal, as I could tell by the grease on his hands, was a fitter. His job was to look after the big Rolls-Royce Merlin engines in the Hurricanes and there was little doubt that he loved them dearly. 'This is a brand-new kite,' he said, laying a greasy hand on the metal wing and stroking it gently. 'It's took somebody *thousands of hours* to build it. And now those silly sods behind their desks back in Cairo 'ave sent it out 'ere where it ain't goin' to last two minutes.'

Eleusis

'Where's the Ops Room?' I asked him.

He pointed to a small wooden hut on the other side of the landing field. Alongside the hut there was a cluster of about thirty tents. I slung my parachute over my shoulder and started to make my way across the field to the hut.

To some extent I was aware of the military mess I had flown in to. I knew that a small British Expeditionary Force, backed up by an equally small air force, had been sent to Greece from Egypt a few months earlier to hold back the Italian invaders, and so long as it was only the Italians they were up against, they had been able to cope. But once the Germans decided to take over, the situation immediately became hopeless. The problem confronting the British now was how to extricate their army from Greece before all the troops were either killed or captured. It was Dunkirk all over again. But it was not receiving the publicity that Dunkirk had received because it was a military bloomer that was best covered up. I guessed that everything the Corporal had just told me was more or less true, but curiously enough none of it worried me in the slightest. I was young enough and starry-eyed enough to look upon this Grecian escapade as nothing more than a grand adventure. The thought that I might never get out of the country alive didn't occur to me. It should have done, and looking back on it now I am surprised that it didn't. Had I paused for a moment and calculated the odds against survival, I would have found that they were about fifty to one and that's enough to give anyone the shakes.

I pushed open the door of the Ops Room hut and went

in. There were three men in there, the Squadron-Leader himself and a Flight-Lieutenant and a wireless-operator Sergeant with ear-phones on. I had never met any of them before. Officially, I had been a member of 80 Squadron for more than six months, but up until now I had not succeeded in getting anywhere near it. The last time I had tried, I had finished up on a bonfire in the Western Desert. The Squadron-Leader had a black moustache and a Distinguished Flying Cross ribbon on his chest. He also had a frowning worried look on his face. 'Oh, hello,' he said. 'We've been expecting you for some time.'

'I'm sorry I'm late,' I said.

'Six months late,' he said. 'You can find yourself a bunk in one of the tents. You'll start flying tomorrow like the rest of them.'

I could see that the man was preoccupied and wished to get rid of me, but I hesitated. It was quite a shock to be dismissed as casually as this. It had been a truly great struggle for me to get back on my feet and join the squadron at last, and I had expected at least a brief 'I'm glad you made it,' or 'I hope you're feeling better.' But this, as I suddenly realized, was a different ball game altogether. This was a place where pilots were disappearing like flies. What difference did an extra one make when you only had fourteen? None whatsoever. What the Squadron-Leader wanted was *a hundred* extra planes and pilots, not one.

I went out of the Ops Rooms hut still carrying my parachute over my shoulder. In the other hand I carried a brown paper-bag that contained all the belongings I had been able to bring with me, a toothbrush, a half-finished tube of toothpaste, a razor, a tube of shaving soap, a spare khaki shirt, a blue cardigan, a pair of pyjamas, my Log Book and my beloved camera. Ever since I was fourteen I had been an enthusiastic photographer, starting in 1930 with an old double-extension plate camera and doing my own developing and enlarging. Now I had a Zeiss Super Ikonta with an f 6.3 Tessar lens.

Out in the Middle East, both in Egypt and in Greece, unless it was winter we dressed in nothing but a khaki shirt and khaki shorts and stockings, and even when we flew we seldom bothered to put on a sweater. The paper-bag I was now carrying, as well as the Log Book and the camera, had been tucked under my legs on the flight over and there had been no room for anything else.

I was to share a tent with another pilot and when I ducked my head low and went in, my companion was sitting on his camp-bed and threading a piece of string into one of his shoes because the shoe-lace had broken. He had a long but friendly face and he introduced himself as David Coke, pronounced Cook. I learnt much later that David Coke came from a very noble family, and today, had he not been killed in his Hurricane later on, he would have been none other than the Earl of Leicester owning one of the most enormous and beautiful stately homes in England, although anyone acting less like a future Earl I have never met. He was warm-hearted and brave and generous, and over the next few weeks we were to become close friends. I sat down on my own camp-bed and began to ask him a few questions.

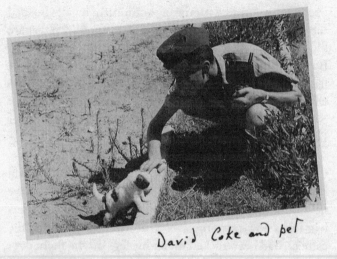

David Coke and pet

'Are things out here really as dicey as I've been told?' I asked him.

'It's absolutely hopeless,' he said, 'but we're plugging on. The German fighters will be within range of us any moment now, and then we'll be outnumbered by about fifty to one. If they don't get us in the air, they'll wipe us out on the ground.'

'Look,' I said, 'I have never been in action in my life. I haven't the foggiest idea what to do if I meet one of them.'

David Coke stared at me as though he were seeing a ghost. He could hardly have looked more startled if I had suddenly announced that I had never been up in an aeroplane before. 'You don't mean to say', he gasped, 'that you've come out to this place of all places with absolutely no experience whatsoever!'

'I'm afraid so,' I said. 'But I expect they'll put me to fly with one of the old hands who'll show me the ropes.'

'You're going to be unlucky,' he said. 'Out here we go up in ones. It hasn't occurred to them that it's better to fly in pairs. I'm afraid you'll be all on your own right from the start. But seriously, have you never even been in a squadron before in your life?'

'Never,' I said.

'Does the CO know this?' he asked me.

'I don't expect he's stopped to think about it,' I said. 'He simply told me I'd start flying tomorrow like all the others.'

'But where on earth have you come from then?' he asked. 'They'd never send a totally inexperienced pilot to a place like this.'

I told him briefly what had been happening to me over the last six months.

'Oh Christ!' he said. 'What a place to start! How many hours do you have on Hurricanes?'

'About seven,' I said.

'Oh, my God!' he cried. 'That means you hardly know how to fly the thing!'

'I don't really,' I said. 'I can do take-offs and landings but I've never exactly tried throwing it around in the air.'

He sat there still not quite able to believe what I was saying.

'Have you been here long?' I asked him.

'Not very,' he said. 'I was in the Battle of Britain before I came here. That was bad enough, but it was peanuts compared to this crazy place. We have no radar here at all and precious little RT. You can only talk to the ground when you are sitting right on top of the aerodrome. And you can't talk to each other at all when you're in the air. There is virtually no communication. The Greeks are our radar. We have a Greek peasant sitting on the top of every mountain for miles around, and when he spots a bunch of German planes he calls up the Ops Room here on a field telephone. That's our radar.'

'Does it work?'

'Now and again it does,' he said. 'But most of our spotters don't know a Messerschmitt from a baby-carriage.' He had managed to thread the string through all the eyes in his shoe and now he started to put the shoe back on his foot.

'Have the Germans really got a thousand planes in Greece?' I asked him.

'It seems likely,' he said. 'Yes, I think they have. You see, Greece is only a beginning for them. After they've taken Greece, they intend to push on south and take Crete as well. I'm sure of that.'

We sat on our camp-beds thinking about the future. I could see that it was going to be a pretty hairy one.

Then David Coke said, 'As you don't seem to know anything at all, I'd better try to help you. What would you like to know?'

'Well, first of all,' I said, 'what do I do when I meet a One-O-Nine?'

'You try to get on his tail,' he said. 'You try to turn in a tighter circle than him. If you let him get on to your tail, you've had it. A Messerschmitt has cannon in its wings.

We've only got bullets, and they aren't even incendiaries. They're just ordinary bullets. The Hun has cannon-shells that explode when they hit you. Our bullets just make little holes in the fuselage. So you've got to hit him smack in the engine to bring him down. He can hit you anywhere at all and the cannon-shell will explode and blow you up.'

I tried to digest what he was saying.

'One other thing,' he said, 'never, absolutely never, take your eyes off your rear-view mirror for more than a few seconds. They come up behind you and they come very fast.'

'I'll try to remember that,' I said. 'What do I do if I meet a bomber? What's the best way to attack him?'

'The bombers you will meet will be mostly Ju 88s,' he said. 'The Ju 88 is a very good aircraft. It is just about as fast as you are and it's got a rear-gunner and a front-gunner. The gunners on a Ju 88 use incendiary tracer bullets and they aim their guns like they're aiming a hose-pipe. They can see where their bullets are going all the time and that makes them pretty deadly. So if you are attacking a Ju 88 from astern, make quite sure you get well below him so the rear-gunner can't hit you. But you won't shoot him down that way. You have to go for one of his engines. And when you are doing that, remember to allow plenty of deflection. Aim well in front of him. Get the nose of his engine on the outer ring of your reflector sight.'

I hardly knew what he was talking about, but I nodded and said, 'Right. I'll try to do that.'

'Oh my God,' he said. 'I can't teach you how to shoot down Germans in one easy lesson. I just wish I could take you up with me tomorrow so I could look after you a bit.'

'Can't you?' I said eagerly. 'We could ask the CO.'

'Not a hope,' he said. 'We always go up singly. Except when we do a sweep, then we all go up together in formation.'

He paused and ran his fingers through his pale-brown hair. 'The trouble here', he said, 'is that the CO doesn't talk much to his pilots. He doesn't even fly with them. He must have flown once because he's got a DFC, but I've never seen him get into a Hurricane. In the Battle of Britain the Squadron-Leader always flew with his squadron. And he gave lots of advice and help to his new pilots. In England you always went up in pairs and a new boy always went up with an experienced man. And in the Battle of Britain we had radar and we had RT that jolly well worked. We could talk to the ground and we could talk to each other all the time in the air. But not here. The big thing to remember here is that you are totally on your own. No one is going to help you, not even the CO. In the Battle of Britain', he added, 'the new boys were very carefully looked after.'

'Has flying finished for the day?' I asked him.

'Yes,' he said. 'It'll be getting dark soon. In fact it's about time for supper. I'll take you along.'

The officers' mess was a tent large enough to contain two long trestle tables, one with food on it and the other where we sat down to eat. The food was tinned beef stew and lumps of bread, and there were bottles of Greek retsina wine to go with it. The Greeks have a trick of disguising a poor quality wine by adding pine resin to it, the idea being that the taste of the resin is not quite so appalling as the taste of the wine. We drank retsina because that was all there was. The other pilots in the squadron, all experienced young men who had nearly been killed many times, treated me just as casually as the Squadron-Leader had. Formalities did not exist in this place. Pilots came and pilots went. The others hardly noticed my presence. No real friendships existed. The way David Coke had treated me was exceptional, but then he was an exceptional person. I realized that nobody else was about to take a beginner like me under his wing. Each man was wrapped up in a cocoon of his own problems, and the sheer effort of trying to stay alive and at the same time doing your duty was concentrating the minds of everyone around me. They were all very quiet. There was no larking about. There were just a few muttered remarks about the pilots who had not come back that day. Nothing else.

There was a notice-board nailed to one of the tent poles in the mess and on it was pinned a single typed sheet with the names of the pilots who were to go on patrol the next morning as well as the times of their take-offs. I learnt from David Coke that a patrol meant stooging around directly above the airfield and waiting for the ground controller to call you up and direct you to a precise area where German planes had been spotted by one of the Greek comedians on top of his mountain. The take-off time against my name was 10 a.m.

When I woke up the next morning, all I could think

about was my ten o'clock take-off time and the fact that I would almost certainly be meeting the Luftwaffe in some form or another and entirely on my own for the first time. Such thoughts as these tend to loosen the bowels and I asked David Coke where I could find the latrines. He told me roughly where they were and I wandered off to find them.

I had been in some fairly primitive lavatories in East Africa, but the 80 Squadron latrines at Elevsis beat the lot. A wide trench six feet deep and sixteen feet long had been dug in the ground. Down the whole length of this trench a round pole had been suspended about four feet above the ground, and I watched in horror as an airman who had got there before me lowered his trousers and attempted to sit on the pole. The trench was so wide that he could hardly reach the pole with his hands. But when he did, he had to turn around and do a sort of backwards leap in the hope of his bottom landing squarely on the pole. Having managed this, but only just, he had to grip the pole with both hands to keep his balance. He lost his balance and over he went backwards into the awful pit. I pulled him out and he hurried away I know not where to try to wash himself. I refused to risk it. I wandered away and found a place behind an olive tree where the wild flowers grew all around me.

At exactly ten o'clock I was strapped into my Hurricane ready for take-off. Several others had gone off singly before me during the past half-hour and had disappeared into the blue Grecian sky. I took off and climbed to 5,000 feet and started circling above the flying field while somebody in the Ops Room tried to contact me on his amazingly inefficient apparatus. My code-name was Blue Four.

Through a storm of static a far-away voice kept saying in my ear-phones, 'Blue Four, can you hear me? Can you hear me?' And I kept replying, 'Yes, but only just.'

'Await orders,' the faint voice said. 'Listen out.'

I cruised around admiring the blue sea to the south and the great mountains to the north, and I was just beginning to think to myself that this was a very nice way to fight a war when the static erupted again and the voice said, 'Blue Four, are you receiving me?'

'Yes,' I said, 'but speak louder please.'

'Bandits over shipping at Khalkis,' the voice said. 'Vector 035 forty miles angels eight.'

'Received,' I said. 'I'm on my way.'

The translation of this simple message, which even I could understand, told me that if I set a course on my compass of thirty-five degrees and flew for a distance of forty miles, I would then, with a bit of luck, intercept the enemy at 8,000 feet, where he was trying to sink ships off a place called Khalkis, wherever that might be.

I set my course and opened the throttle and hoped I was doing everything right. I checked my ground speed and calculated that it would take me between ten and eleven minutes to travel forty miles to this place called Khalkis. I cleared the top of the mountain range with 500 feet to spare, and as I went over it I saw a single solitary goat, brown and white, wandering on the bare rock. 'Hello goat,' I said aloud into my oxygen mask, 'I'll bet you don't know the Germans are going to have you for supper before you're very much older.'

To which, as I realized as soon as I'd said it, the goat might very well have answered, 'And the same to you, my boy. You're no better off than I am.'

Then I saw below me in the distance a kind of water-way or fjord and a little cluster of houses on the shore. Khalkis, I thought. It must be Khalkis. There was one large cargo ship in the waterway and as I was looking at it I saw an enormous fountain of spray erupting high in the air close to the ship. I had never seen a bomb exploding in the water before, but I had seen plenty of photographs of it happening. I looked up into the sky above the ship, but I could see nothing there. I kept staring. I figured that if a bomb had been dropped, someone must be up there dropping it. Two more mighty cascades of water leapt up around the ship. Then suddenly I spotted the bombers. I saw the small black dots wheeling and circling in the sky high above the ship. It gave me quite a shock. It was my first-ever sight of the enemy from my own plane. Quickly I turned the brass ring of my firing-button from 'safe' to 'fire'. I switched on my reflector-sight and a pale red circle of light with two crossbars appeared suspended in the air in front of my face. I headed straight for the little dots.

Half a minute later, the dots had resolved themselves into black twin-engine bombers. They were Ju 88s. I counted six of them. I glanced above and around them but I could see no fighters protecting them. I remember being absolutely cool and unafraid. My one wish was to do my job properly and not to make a hash of it.

There are three men in a Ju 88, which gives it three pairs of eyes. So six Ju 88s have no less than eighteen pairs of eyes scanning the sky. Had I been more experienced, I would have realized this much earlier on and before going any closer I would have swung round so that the sun was behind me. I would also have climbed very fast to get well above them before attacking. I did neither of these things. I simply went straight for them at the same height as they were and with the strong Grecian sun right in my own eyes.

They spotted me while I was still half a mile away and suddenly all six bombers banked away steeply and dived straight for a great mass of mountains behind Khalkis.

I had been warned never to push my throttle 'through the gate' except in a real emergency. Going 'through the gate' meant that the big Rolls-Royce engine would produce absolute maximum revs, and three minutes was the limit of time it could tolerate such stress. OK, I thought, this is an emergency. I rammed the throttle right 'through the gate'. The engine roared and the Hurricane leapt forward. I began to catch up fast on the bombers. They had now gone into a line-abreast formation which, as I was soon to discover, allowed all six of their rear-gunners to fire at me simultaneously.

The mountains behind Khalkis are wild and black and very rugged and the Germans went right in among them flying well below the summits. I followed, and sometimes we flew so close to the cliffs I could see the startled vultures taking off as we roared past. I was still gaining on them, and when I was about 200 yards behind them, all six rear-gunners in the Ju 88s began shooting at me. As

David Coke had warned, they were using tracer and out of each one of the six rear turrets came a brilliant shaft of orange-red flame. Six different shafts of bright orange-red came arcing towards me from six different turrets. They were like very thin streams of coloured water from six different hosepipes. I found them fascinating to watch. The deadly orange-red streams seemed to start out quite slowly from the turrets and I could see them bending in the air as they came towards me and then suddenly they were flashing past my cockpit like fireworks.

I was just beginning to realize that I had got myself into the worst possible position for an attacking fighter to be in when suddenly the passage between the mountains on either side narrowed and the Ju 88s were forced to go into line astern. This meant that only the last one in the line could shoot at me. That was better. Now there was only a single stream of orange-red bullets coming towards me. David Coke had said, 'Go for one of his engines.' I went a little closer and by jiggling my plane this way and that I managed to get the starboard engine of the bomber into my reflector-sight. I aimed a bit ahead of the engine and pressed the button. The Hurricane gave a small shudder as the eight Brownings in the wings all opened up together, and a second later I saw a huge piece of his metal engine-cowling the size of a dinner-tray go flying up into the air. Good heavens, I thought, I've hit him! I've actually hit him! Then black smoke came pouring out of his engine and very slowly, almost in slow motion, the bomber winged over to starboard and began to lose height. I throttled back. He was well below me now. I could see him clearly by squinting down out of my cockpit. He wasn't diving and he wasn't spinning either. He was turning slowly over and over like a leaf, the black smoke pouring out from the starboard engine. Then I saw one . . . two . . . three people jump out of the fuselage and go tumbling earthwards with legs and arms outstretched in grotesque attitudes, and a moment later one . . . two . . . three parachutes billowed open and began floating gently down between the cliffs towards the narrow valley below.

I watched spellbound. I couldn't believe that I had actually shot down a German bomber. But I was immensely relieved to see the parachutes.

I opened the throttle again and began to climb up above the mountains. The five remaining Ju 88s had disappeared. I looked around me and all I could see were craggy peaks in every direction. I set a course due south and fifteen minutes later I was landing at Elevsis. I parked my Hurricane and clambered out. I had been away for exactly one hour. It seemed like ten minutes. I walked slowly all the way round my Hurricane looking for damage. Miraculously the fuselage seemed to be completely unscathed. The only mark those six rear-gunners had been able to make on a sitting-duck like me was a single neat round hole in one of the blades of my wooden propeller. I shouldered my parachute and walked across to the Ops Rooms hut. I was feeling pretty good.

As before, the Squadron-Leader was in the hut and so was the wireless-operator Sergeant with the ear-phones on his head. The Squadron-Leader looked up at me and frowned. 'How did you get on?' he asked.

'I got one Ju 88,' I said, trying to keep the pride and satisfaction out of my voice.

'Are you sure?' he asked. 'Did you see it hit the ground?'

'No,' I said. 'But I saw the crew jump out and open their parachutes.'

'OK,' he said. 'That sounds definite enough.'

'I'm afraid there's a bullet hole in my prop,' I said.

'Oh well,' he said. 'You'd better tell the rigger to patch it up as best he can.'

That was the end of our interview. I expected more, a pat on the back or a 'Jolly good show' and a smile, but as I've said before, he had many things on his mind including Pilot Officer Holman who had gone out thirty minutes before me and hadn't come back. He wasn't going to come back.

David Coke had also been flying that morning and I found him sitting on his camp-bed doing nothing. I told him about my trip.

'Never do that again,' he said. 'Never sit on the tails of six Ju 88s and expect to get away with it because next time you won't.'

'What happened to you?' I asked him.

'I got one One-O-Nine,' he said. He said it as calmly as if he were telling me he'd caught a fish in the river across the road. 'It's going to be very dangerous out there from now on,' he added. 'The One-O-Nines and the One-One-O's are swarming like wasps. You'd better be very careful next time.'

'I'll try,' I said. 'I'll do my best.'

The Ammunition Ship

The next morning I was ordered to go on patrol at six o'clock. I took off dead on time and climbed in a tight circle to 5,000 feet over the airfield. The sun had just cleared the horizon and I could see the Parthenon glowing white and wonderful on the famous hill above Athens. My radio crackled almost at once and the voice from the Ops Room gave me precisely the same instructions it had given me the day before. I was to proceed to Khalkis where the enemy was again bombing the shipping. Five Hurricanes had taken off before me that morning and I had watched them all being sent away one by one in different directions. The enemy was all around us now and we were having to spread ourselves extremely thin. Khalkis, it seemed, was reserved for me.

I had learnt the night before from someone in the Ops Room that the big cargo vessel lying off Khalkis was an ammunition ship. It was loaded to the brim with high explosives and the Germans had found out about it. The brave Greeks, who were trying their best to offload the bullets and bombs and whatever other fireworks there were on board, knew that it only needed one direct hit to blow everything sky-high, including the town of Khalkis and most of its inhabitants.

I arrived over Khalkis at 6.15 a.m. The big cargo ship was still there and there was now a lighter alongside it. A derrick was hoisting a large crate up from the ship's forward hold and lowering it into the lighter. I searched the sky for enemy planes but I couldn't see any. A man on the deck of the ship looked up and waved his cap at me. I slid back the roof of my cockpit and waved back at him.

I am writing this forty-five years afterwards, but I still retain an absolutely clear picture of Khalkis and how it looked from a few thousand feet up on a bright-blue early April morning. The little town with its sparkling white houses and red-tiled roofs stood on the edge of the waterway, and behind the town I could see the jagged grey-black mountains where I had chased the Ju 88s the day before. Inland, I could see a wide valley and there were green fields in the valley and among the fields there were splashes of the most brilliant yellow I had ever seen. The whole landscape looked as though it had been painted on to the surface of the earth by Vincent Van Gogh. On all sides and wherever I looked there was this dazzling panorama of beauty, and for a moment or two I was so overwhelmed by it all that I didn't see the big Ju 88 screaming up at me from below until he was almost touching the underbelly of my plane. He was climbing right up at me with the tracer pouring like yellow fire out of his blunt perspex nose and in that thousandth of a second I actually saw the German front-gunner crouching over his gun and gripping it with both hands as he squeezed the trigger. I saw his brown helmet and his pale face with no goggles over the eyes and he was wearing some sort of a black flying-suit. I yanked my stick back so hard the Hurricane shot vertically upwards like a rocket. The violent change of direction blacked me out completely, and when my sight returned my plane was at the top of a vertical climb and standing on its tail with almost no forward movement at all. My engine was spluttering and beginning to vibrate. I've been hit, I thought, I've been hit in the engine. I rammed the stick hard forward and prayed she would respond. By some miracle, the aircraft dropped its nose and the engine began to pick up and within a few seconds the marvellous machine was flying straight and level once again.

But where was the German?

I looked down and spotted him about 1,000 feet below me. His wings were silhouetted against the blue water of the bay, and I could hardly believe it but he was actually ignoring me completely and was beginning to make his bombing run over the ammunition ship! I opened the throttle and dived after him. In eight seconds I was on him, but I was diving so steeply and so fast that when the great grey-green bomber came into my sights, I was only able to get in a very short burst and then I was past him and yanking back hard on the stick to stop myself from diving on into the water.

I had made a mess of it. For the second time running I had gone barging in to the attack without pausing for just a fraction of a second to work out the best way of doing things. I roared upwards again and banked round sharply to have another go at him. He was still heading for the ship. But then something quite startling happened. I saw his nose drop suddenly downwards and he went plunging head first in an absolutely straight vertical line into the blue waters of Khalkis Bay. He hit the water not far from the ship and there was a tremendous white splash and then the waves closed over him and he was gone.

How on earth did I manage that? I wondered. The only explanation I could think of was that a lucky bullet must have hit the pilot so that he slumped over his stick and pushed it forward and down she went. I could see several Greek seamen on the deck of the ship waving their caps at me and I waved back at them. That is how stupid I was. I quite literally sat there in my cockpit waving away at the Greek seamen below, forgetting that I was in a hostile sky that could be seething with German aircraft. When I stopped waving and looked around me, I saw something that made me jump. There were aeroplanes everywhere. They were diving and climbing and turning and banking wherever I looked, and they all had black and white crosses on their bodies and black swastikas on their tails. I knew right away what they were. They were the dreaded little German Messerschmitt 109 fighters. I had never seen one before but I knew darn well what they looked like. I swear there must have been thirty or forty of them within a few hundred yards of me. It was like having a swarm of wasps around your head and quite honestly I did not know what to do next. It would have been suicide to stay and fight, and in any event my duty was to save my plane at all costs. The Germans had hundreds of fighters. We had only a few left.

I shoved the stick forward and opened the throttle and dived flat out for the ground. I had a feeling that if I could fly very low and very dangerously over the treetops and hedges then the German pilots might not be prepared to take the same risk.

When I levelled out from the dive I was doing about 300 miles an hour and flying some twenty feet above the ground. That is below rooftop level and is a fairly hairy thing to do at such a speed. But I was in a hairy situation. I was flying up the yellow Van Gogh valley now and a swift glance in my rear-view mirror showed a bunch of 109s right on my tail. I went lower. I went so low I actually had to leapfrog over the small olive trees that were scattered around everywhere. Then I took a huge but calculated risk and went lower still, almost brushing the grass in the fields. I knew the Germans couldn't hit me unless they came down to my height, and even if they did, the concentration required to fly a plane very fast at almost ground level was so great they would hardly be able to shoot straight at the same time. You may not believe it but I can remember having literally to lift my plane just a tiny fraction to clear a stone wall, and once there was a herd of brown cows in front of me and I'm not sure I didn't clip some of their horns with my propeller as I skimmed over them.

Suddenly the Messerschmitts had had enough. In the mirror I saw them pull away one after the other, and oh the relief of being able to climb up to a safer height and to go whistling back over the mountains to Elevsis.

The bad news I brought with me to the squadron was that the German fighter planes were now within range of us. In their hundreds they could reach our airfield any time they liked.

The Battle of Athens – the Twentieth of April

The next three days, 17, 18 and 19 April 1941, are a little blurred in my memory. The fourth day, 20 April, is not blurred at all. My Log Book records that from Elevsis aerodrome

on 17 April I went up three times
on 18 April I went up twice
on 19 April I went up three times
on 20 April I went up four times.

Each one of those sorties meant running across the airfield to wherever the Hurricane was parked (often 200 yards away), strapping in, starting up, taking off, flying to a particular area, engaging the enemy, getting home again, landing, reporting to the Ops Room and then making sure the aircraft was refuelled and rearmed immediately so as to be ready for another take-off.

Twelve separate sorties against the enemy in four days is a fairly hectic pace by any standards, and each one of us knew that every time a sortie was made, somebody was probably going to get killed, either the Hun or the man in the Hurricane. I used to figure that the betting on every flight was about even money against my coming back, but in reality it wasn't even money at all. When you are out-numbered by at least ten to one on nearly every occasion, then a bookmaker, had there been one on the aerodrome, would probably have been willing to lay something like five to one against your return on each trip.

Like all the others, I was always sent up alone. I wished I could sometimes have had a friendly wing-tip alongside me, and more importantly, a second pair of eyes to help me watch the sky behind and above. But we didn't have enough aircraft for luxuries of that sort.

Sometimes I was over Piraeus harbour, chasing the Ju 88s that were bombing the shipping there. Sometimes I was around the Lamia area, trying to deter the Luftwaffe from blasting away at our retreating army, although how anyone could think that a single Hurricane was going to make any difference out there was beyond me. Once or twice, I met the bombers over Athens itself, where they usually came along in groups of twelve at a time. On three occasions my Hurricane was badly shot up, but the riggers in 80 Squadron were magicians at patching up holes in the fuselage or mending a broken spar. We were so frantically busy during these four days that individual victories were hardly noticed or counted. And unlike the fighter aircraft back in Britain, we had no camera-guns to tell us whether we had hit anything or not. We seemed to spend our entire time running out to the aircraft, scrambling, dashing off to some place or other, chasing the Hun, pressing the firing-button, landing back at Elevsis and going up again.

My Log Book records that on 17 April we lost Flight-Sergeant Cottingham and Flight-Sergeant Rivelon and both their aircraft.

On 18 April Pilot Officer Oofy Still went out and did not return. I remember Oofy Still as a smiling young man with freckles and red hair.

That left us with twelve Hurricanes and twelve pilots with which to cover the whole of Greece from 19 April onwards.

As I have said, 17, 18 and 19 April seem to be all jumbled up together in my memory, and no single incident has remained vividly with me. But 20 April was quite different. I went up four separate times on 20 April, but it was the first of these sorties that I will never forget. It stands out like a sheet of flame in my memory.

On that day, somebody behind a desk in Athens or Cairo had decided that for once our entire force of Hurricanes, all twelve of us, should go up together. The inhabitants of Athens, so it seemed, were getting jumpy and it was assumed that the sight of us all flying overhead would boost their morale. Had I been an inhabitant of Athens at that time, with a German army of over 100,000 advancing swiftly on the city, not to mention a Luftwaffe of about 1,000 planes all within bombing distance, I would have been pretty jumpy myself, and the sight of twelve lonely Hurricanes flying overhead would have done little to boost my morale.

However, on 20 April, on a golden springtime morning at ten o'clock, all twelve of us took off one after the other and got into a tight formation over Elevsis airfield. Then we headed for Athens, which was no more than four minutes' flying time away.

I had never flown a Hurricane in formation before.

Even in training I had only done formation flying once in a little Tiger Moth. It is not a particularly tricky business if you have had plenty of practice, but if you are new to the game and if you are required to fly within a few feet of your neighbour's wing-tip, it is a dicey experience. You keep your position by jiggling the throttle back and forth the whole time and by being extremely delicate on the rudder-bar and the stick. It is not so bad when everyone is flying straight and level, but when the entire formation is doing steep turns all the time, it becomes very difficult for a fellow as inexperienced as I was.

Round and round Athens we went, and I was so busy trying to prevent my starboard wing-tip from scraping against the plane next to me that this time I was in no mood to admire the grand view of the Parthenon or any of the other famous relics below me. Our formation was being led by Flight-Lieutenant Pat Pattle. Now Pat Pattle was a legend in the RAF. At least he was a legend around Egypt and the Western Desert and in the mountains of Greece. He was far and away the greatest fighter ace the Middle East was ever to see, with an astronomical number of victories to his credit. It was even said that he had shot down more planes than any of the famous and glamorized Battle of Britain aces, and this was probably true. I myself had never spoken to him and I am sure he hadn't the faintest idea who I was. I wasn't anybody. I was just a new face in a squadron whose pilots took very little notice of each other anyway. But I had observed the famous Flight-Lieutenant Pattle in the mess tent several times. He was a very small man and very soft-spoken, and he possessed the deeply wrinkled doleful face of a cat who knew that all nine of its lives had already been used up.

On that morning of 20 April, Flight-Lieutenant Pattle, the ace of aces, who was leading our formation of twelve Hurricanes over Athens, was evidently assuming that we could all fly as brilliantly as he could, and he led us one hell of a dance around the skies above the city. We were flying at about 9,000 feet and we were doing our very best to show the people of Athens how powerful and noisy and brave we were, when suddenly the whole sky around us seemed to explode with German fighters. They came down on us from high above, not only 109s but also the twin-engined 110s. Watchers on the ground say that there cannot have been fewer than 200 of them around us that morning. We broke formation and now it was every man for himself. What has become known as the Battle of Athens began.

I find it almost impossible to describe vividly what happened during the next half-hour. I don't think any fighter pilot has ever managed to convey what it is like to be up there in a long-lasting dog-fight. You are in a small metal cockpit where just about everything is made of riveted aluminium. There is a plexiglass hood over your head and a sloping bullet-proof windscreen in front of you. Your right hand is on the stick and your right thumb is on the brass firing-button on the top loop of the stick. Your left hand is on the throttle and your two feet are on the rudder-bar. Your body is attached by shoulder-straps and belt to the parachute you are sitting on, and a second pair of shoulder-straps and a belt are holding you rigidly in the cockpit. You can turn your head and you can move your arms and legs, but the rest of your body is strapped so tightly into the tiny cockpit that you cannot move. Between your face and the windscreen, the round orange-red circle of the reflector-sight glows brightly.

Some people do not realize that although a Hurricane had eight guns in its wings, those guns were all immobile. You did not aim the guns, you aimed the plane. The guns themselves were carefully sighted and tested beforehand on the ground so that the bullets from each gun would converge at a point about 150 yards ahead. Thus, using your reflector-sight, you aimed the plane at the target and pressed the button. To aim accurately in this way requires skilful flying, especially as you are usually in a steep turn and going very fast when the moment comes.

Over Athens on that morning, I can remember seeing our tight little formation of Hurricanes all peeling away and disappearing among the swarms of enemy aircraft, and from then on, wherever I looked I saw an endless blur of enemy fighters whizzing towards me from every side. They came from above and they came from behind and they made frontal attacks from dead ahead, and I threw my Hurricane around as best I could and whenever a Hun came into my sights, I pressed the button. It was truly the most breathless and in a way the most exhilarating time I have ever had in my life. I caught glimpses of planes with black smoke pouring from their engines. I saw planes with pieces of metal flying off their fuselages. I saw the bright-red flashes coming from the wings of the Messerschmitts as they fired their guns, and once I saw a man whose Hurricane was in flames climb calmly out on to a wing and jump off. I stayed with them until I had no ammunition left in my guns. I had done a lot of shooting, but whether I had shot anyone down or had even hit any of them I could not say. I did not dare to pause for even a fraction of a second to observe results. The sky was so full of aircraft that half my time was spent in actually avoiding collisions. I am quite sure that the German planes must have often got in each other's way because there were so many of them, and that, together with the fact that there were so few of us, probably saved quite a number of our skins.

When I finally had to break away and dive for home, I knew my Hurricane had been hit. The controls were very soggy and there was no response at all to the rudder. But you can turn a plane after a fashion with the ailerons alone, and that is how I managed to steer the plane back. Thank heavens the undercarriage came down when I engaged the lever, and I landed more or less safely at Elevsis. I taxied to a parking place, switched off the engine and slid back the hood. I sat there for at least one minute, taking deep gasping breaths. I was quite literally overwhelmed by the feeling that I had been into the very bowels of the fiery furnace and had managed to claw my way out. All around me now the sun was shining and wild flowers were blossoming in the grass of the airfield, and I thought how fortunate I was to be seeing the good earth again. Two airmen, a fitter and a rigger, came trotting up to my machine. I watched them as they walked slowly all the way round it. Then the rigger, a balding middle-aged man, looked up at me and said, 'Blimey mate, this kite's got so many 'oles in it, it looks like it's made out of chicken-wire!'

I undid my straps and eased myself upright in the cock-pit. 'Do your best with it,' I said. 'I'll be needing it again very soon.'

I remember walking over to the little wooden Operations Room to report my return and as I made my way slowly across the grass of the landing field I suddenly realized that the whole of my body and all my clothes were dripping with sweat. The weather was warm in Greece at that time of year and we wore only khaki shorts and khaki shirt and stockings even when we flew, but now those shorts and shirt and stockings had all changed colour and were quite black with wetness. So was my hair when I removed my helmet. I had never sweated like that before in my life, even after a game of squash or rugger. The water was pouring off me and dripping to the ground. At the door of the Ops Room three or four other pilots were standing around and I noticed that each one of them was as wet as I was. I put a cigarette between my lips and struck a match. Then I found that my hand was shaking so much I couldn't put the flame to the end of the cigar-ette. The doctor, who was standing nearby, came up and lit it for me. I looked at my hands again. It was ridiculous the way they were shaking. It was embarrassing. I looked at the other pilots. They were all holding cigarettes and their hands were all shaking as much as mine were. But I was feeling pretty good. I had stayed up there for thirty minutes and they hadn't got me.

They got five of our twelve Hurricanes in that battle. One of our pilots baled out and was saved. Four were killed. Among the dead was the great Pat Pattle, all his lucky lives used up at last. And Flight-Lieutenant Timber Woods, the second most experienced pilot in the squadron, was also among those killed. Greek observers on the ground as well as our own people on the airstrip saw the five Hurricanes going down in smoke, but they also saw something else. They saw twenty-two Messerschmitts shot down during that battle, although none of us ever knew who got what.

So we now had seven half-serviceable Hurricanes left in Greece, and with these we were expected to give air cover to the entire British Expeditionary Force which

Elevsis

was about to be evacuated along the coast. The whole thing was a ridiculous farce.

I wandered over to my tent. There was a canvas wash-basin outside the tent, one of those folding things that stand on three wooden legs, and David Coke was bending over it, sloshing water on his face. He was naked except for a small towel round his waist and his skin was very white.

'So you made it,' he said, not looking up.

'So did you,' I said.

'It was a bloody miracle,' he said. 'I'm shaking all over. What happens next?'

'I think we're going to get killed,' I said.

'So do I,' he said. 'You can have the basin in a moment. I left a bit of water in the jug just in case you happened to come back.'

The Last Day But One

But the twentieth of April was not over yet.

I was standing quite naked beside the three-legged basin outside the tent with David Coke trying to wash off some of the sweat of battle when *boom bang woomph wham rat-tat-tat-tat-tat* a tremendous explosion of noises slammed into us overhead with a rattle of machine-guns and a roar of engines. I jumped and David jumped and looking up we saw a long line of Messerschmitt 109s coming straight at us very fast and low with guns blazing. We threw ourselves flat on the grass and waited for the worst.

I had never been ground-strafed before and I can promise you it is not a nice experience, especially when they catch you out in the open with your pants down. You lie there watching the bullets running through the grass and kicking up chunks of turf all around you and unless there is a deep ditch nearby there is nothing you can do to protect yourself. The 109s were coming at us in line astern, one after the other, skimming just over the tents, and as each one roared past overhead I could feel the wind of its slipstream on my naked back. I remember twisting my head sideways to watch them and I could see the pilots sitting upright in their cockpits, black helmets on and khaki-coloured oxygen masks over their noses and mouths, and one pilot was sporting a bright yellow scarf around his neck tucked neatly into his open shirt.

They wore no goggles and once or twice I caught a glimpse of a pair of German eyes bright with concentration and staring directly ahead.

'We've had it now!' David was shouting. 'They'll get every one of our planes!'

'To hell with the planes!' I shouted back. 'What about us?'

'They're after the Hurricanes,' David shouted. 'They'll pick them off one by one. You watch.'

The Germans knew that the few planes we had left in Greece had just landed after a battle and were now refuelling, which is the classic moment for a ground-strafe. But what they did not know was that our airfield defences consisted of no more than a single Bofors gun tucked away somewhere in the rocks behind our tents. Most front-line aerodromes in those days were heavily protected against low-level attacks and because of this no pilot enjoyed going on a ground-strafe. I did some of it myself later on and I didn't like it one bit. You are flying so fast and so low that if you happen to get hit there is very little you can do to save yourself. The Germans couldn't know we had only one wretched gun to protect the whole aerodrome so they played it safe and made just that one swift pass over our field and then beat it for home.

They had disappeared as suddenly as they had arrived, and when they had gone the silence across our flying field was amazing. I wondered for a moment whether perhaps everyone had been killed except David and me. We stood up and surveyed the scene. Then several voices began shouting for stretchers and over by the Ops Hut I could see someone with blood on his clothes being helped towards the doctor's tent. But the surprise of the moment was that our single Bofors gun had actually managed to hit one of the Messerschmitts. We could see him across the aerodrome about forty feet up with black smoke and orange flames pouring from his engine. He was gliding in silently for an attempted landing, and David and I stood watching him as he made a steep turn in towards the field.

'That poor sod will be roasted alive if he doesn't hurry,' David said.

The plane hit the ground on its belly with a fearful scrunch of tearing metal and it slid on for about thirty

Me 109 crashed, Elevsis

yards before stopping. I saw several of our people running out to help the pilot and someone had a red fire-extinguisher in his hand and then they were out of sight in the black smoke and trying to get the German out of the plane. When we saw them again they were hauling him by his arms away from the fire and then a pick-up truck drove out and they put him in the back.

But what of our own planes? We could see them in the distance scattered around the perimeter of the airfield at their dispersal points and not one of them was burning.

'They were in such a bloody hurry I think they've missed them altogether,' David said.

'I think so, too,' I said.

Then the Duty Officer was running between the tents and shouting, 'All pilots to their aircraft! All aircraft to scramble at once! Hurry up there! Get a move on!' He ran past David and me shouting, 'Get your clothes on, you two! Get out there at the double and get your planes in the air!'

It was common practice for a second wave of ground-strafers to come in and attack soon after the first, and the CO rightly wanted our planes in the air before they arrived. David and I flung on shirts and shorts and shoes and dashed towards our Hurricanes, and as I ran I was wondering whether my own plane was even capable of taking off again so soon after the last battle. Less than one hour had gone by since I had landed. When I reached the Hurricane, there were three airmen fussing around the fuselage, including our Flight-Sergeant rigger.

'Have you repaired the rudder?' I shouted at him.

'We've put a new wire in,' the Flight-Sergeant said. 'It was cut clean through.'

'Is she refuelled and rearmed?'

'All ready for you,' the Flight-Sergeant said.

I gave the plane a quick once over. It was remarkable what they had managed to do in so little time. Bullet holes had been stopped up and torn metal had been flattened out and cracks had been filled and there were little patches of red canvas over all eight of the gun ports on the leading edges of the wings, showing that the guns had been serviced and rearmed. I climbed into the cockpit and the Flight-Sergeant came up on to the wing to help me strap in. 'You want to be careful out there now,' he said. 'They're swarming like gnats all over the sky.'

'You'd better be careful yourself,' I said. 'I'd rather be in the air than down here next time they come in.'

He gave me a friendly pat on the back and then slid the hood closed over my head.

It was astonishing that the ground-strafers had not hit a single one of our Hurricanes, and all seven of us got safely up into the air and circled the flying field for about an hour. We were hoping now that they would come back again then we could swoop on them from above and the whole thing would have been a piece of cake. They did not return and down we went once more and landed.

But the twentieth of April was still not over.

I went up twice more during that afternoon, both times to tangle with the clouds of Ju 88s that were bombing the shipping over Piraeus, and by the time evening came I was a very tired young man.

That night we were told (and by we I mean the seven remaining pilots in the squadron) that at first light the next morning we were to take off and fly to a very secret small landing field about thirty miles along the coast. It was clear that if we stayed another day at Elevsis we would be wiped out, planes and all. We crowded around a table in the mess tent and by the light of a paraffin lamp someone, I think it was the squadron Adjutant, tried to show us where this secret landing field was. 'It's right on the edge of the coast,' he said, 'beside a little village called Megara. You can't miss it. It's the only flat bit of land around.'

'Are we going to operate from there?' someone asked.

'God knows,' the Adjutant said.

'But what do we do after we've landed?' we asked him. 'Will there be *anybody* there except us?'

'Just get the hell out of here at dawn tomorrow and go there,' the wretched man said.

'But what's the point of it all?' someone said. 'Right at this moment we have seven quite decent Hurricanes and if we hang around with them here in this crazy country they are certain to be destroyed on the ground or shot down in the air in the next couple of days. So why don't we fly them all to Crete tomorrow morning and save them for better things? We'd be there in an hour and a half. And from Crete we could fly them to Egypt. I'll bet they could use seven extra Hurricanes in the Western Desert.'

'Just do as you're told,' the Adjutant said. 'Our job is to keep these seven planes going so that we can give air cover to the army which is about to be evacuated off the coast by the navy.'

'With seven machines!' a young pilot said. 'And flying out of a little field along the coast with no fitters and no riggers and no refuelling wagons! It's ridiculous!'

The Adjutant looked at the young pilot and said simply, 'It's not my idea. I'm only passing on orders.'

David Coke said, 'Will anyone be at this place Megara when we arrive at dawn tomorrow?'

'I don't think so,' the Adjutant said.

'So what are we supposed to do? Just sit around on the grass?'

'Look,' the poor Adjutant said, 'if I knew any more, I'd tell you.' He was about forty, a volunteer, too old for flying, and he had been a seller of agricultural implements before the war. He was a good man, but he was as much in the dark as we were. 'They're going to come over here and shoot this place to pieces tomorrow,' he went on. 'All of us, ground-crews included, are pulling out tonight. By the time you get up tomorrow morning the place will be empty. So make sure you all get away the moment there's enough daylight for a take-off. Don't hang about.'

'Where are you all going to?' somebody asked him. 'Are you joining us at our secret little landing ground?'

'No,' he said, 'we're not. We're going farther along the coast. I don't even know myself where it is.'

'Is it another secret landing field?'

'I think it is,' the Adjutant said.

'Then why don't we fly there direct tomorrow?'

someone asked him. 'What's the point of going to this deserted Megara place?'

'*I don't know!*' the Adjutant shouted, exasperated.

'Where's the CO?' somebody asked.

'*That's enough!*' the Adjutant shouted. 'Go to bed all of you and get some sleep!'

One of us had an alarm clock and the next morning he woke us all up at 4.30 a.m. When I stepped out of our tent, Elevsis aerodrome lay silent and deserted in the pale half-light of the dawn. All tents except for those being used by the pilots had been struck and taken away. Only the old corrugated-iron hangar and the Ops Room hut and a few other wooden huts remained. The seven of us assembled in a little group, rubbing our hands together in the chill morning air. 'Isn't there a hot drink anywhere?' someone said.

There wasn't anything.

'We'd better get going,' David Coke said.

It was about 5 a.m. when we walked across the deserted and silent landing field to our planes. I think all of us felt very lonely at that moment. An aircraft is never unattended when you go out to it. There is always a fitter or a rigger to pull the chocks away from the wheels after you have started the engine. And if the engine won't start or if the batteries are low, someone brings along the trolley and plugs it in to give your batteries a boost. But there was nobody around. Not a soul. The top rim of the sun was just coming up above the hills beyond Athens and little sparks of sunlight were glinting on the dew in the grass.

I climbed into my Hurricane and hooked up all the straps. I switched on, set the mixture to 'rich' and pressed the starter button. The airscrew began to turn slowly and then the big Merlin engine gave a couple of coughs and started up. I looked around for the other six. They had all managed to get started and were taxiing out for take-off.

The seven of us assembled at about 1,000 feet over the aerodrome and then we flew off along the coast to look for our secret landing strip. Soon we were circling the little village of Megara, and we saw a green field alongside the village and there was a man on an ancient steam-roller rolling out a kind of makeshift landing strip across the field. He looked up as we flew over and then he

My Hurricane at Megara

drove his steam-roller to one side and we landed our planes on the bumpy field and taxied in among some olive trees for cover. The cover was not very good, so we broke branches off the olive trees and draped them over the wings of our planes, hoping to make them less conspicuous from the air. Even so, I figured that the first German to fly over would be sure to see us and then it would be curtains.

The time was 5.15 a.m. There was not a soul on the field except for the man sitting on his steam-roller. We wondered what we ought to do next. If our planes were going to be strafed, then the further away from them we were the better, just so long as we kept them in view. There was a stony ridge about 200 feet high between us and the sea and we decided that this might be as safe a vantage point as any. So up we went and when we got to the top we sat down on the big smooth white boulders and lit cigarettes. Immediately below us and to one side lay the olive grove with the seven Hurricanes half-hidden but still pretty conspicuous among the trees. To the other side lay the blue Gulf of Athens, and I could have thrown a stone into the water it was so close.

A large oil tanker was lying about 500 yards off the shore.

'I wouldn't want to be on that tanker,' somebody said.

Somebody else said, 'Why doesn't the silly sod get the hell out of here? Hasn't he heard about the Germans?'

In a way it was very pleasant to be sitting high up on that rocky ridge early on a bright blue Grecian morning in April. We were young and quite fearless. We were undaunted by the thought that there were only seven of us with seven Hurricanes on a bare field and fifty miles to the north about one half of the entire German Air Force was trying to hunt us down. From where we sat we had a fine view of the Bay of Athens and the blue-green sea and the crazy oil tanker lying at anchor.

Breakfast-time came but there was no breakfast. Then we heard the roar of aircraft engines close by and a group of some thirty 109s came whistling very low over the village of Megara, not half a mile away from us. They flew on, heading straight for Elevsis, the place we had left at the crack of dawn. We had got out just in time.

Only a few minutes later, a bunch of Stuka dive-bombers flew directly over our heads at about 3,000 feet, going straight towards the tanker, and above them a host of protective fighters were swarming like locusts.

'Get down!' somebody shouted. 'Hide under the rocks and keep still! Don't let them see us!'

But surely, I thought, they would see our planes in the olive grove? They were by no means completely hidden.

The Stukas came over in line astern and when the leader was directly above the oil tanker he dropped his nose and went into a screaming vertical dive. We lay among the boulders on top of the ridge watching the first Stuka. Faster and faster it went and we could hear the engine note changing from a roar to a scream as the plane dived absolutely vertically down upon the tanker. To me it looked as though the pilot was aiming to dive his plane straight into the funnel of the ship, but he pulled out just in time and then I saw the bomb coming out of the belly of the plane. It was a big black lump of metal and it fell quite slowly right on to the tanker's forward deck. The Stuka was well away and skimming over the sea as the bomb exploded, and when the great flash came, the whole ship seemed to lift about ten feet out of the water, and already a second Stuka was screaming down followed by a third and a fourth and a fifth.

Only five Stukas dived on to that tanker. The remainder stayed up high and watched because the ship was already blazing from end to end. We were very close to the whole thing, not more than 500 yards away, and when the tanks blew open, the oil spread out over the surface of the water and turned the ocean into a fiery lake. We could see half a dozen of the crew climbing on to the rails and jumping over the side and we heard their screams as they were roasted alive in the flames.

Up above us the Stukas which hadn't dived turned round and headed for home and the escorting fighters went with them. Soon they were all out of sight and the only sounds we heard were the hissing noises of water meeting fire all along the sides of the stricken tanker.

We had seen plenty of bombings in our time, but we had never seen men jumping into a burning sea to be roasted and boiled alive like that. It shook us all.

'It doesn't seem as though anybody has any brains around here,' somebody said. 'Why didn't the Greeks tell that tanker Captain to get the hell out?'

'Why doesn't someone tell us what to do next?' somebody else said.

'Because they don't know,' another voice said.

'Seriously,' I said, 'why don't we all just take off and fly to Crete? We've got full tanks.'

'That's a bloody good idea,' David Coke said. 'Then we can refuel and fly to Egypt. They've hardly got any Hurricanes at all in the Desert. These seven would be worth their weight in gold.'

'You know what I think,' a young man called Dowding said, 'I think someone wants to be able to say that the brave RAF in Greece fought gallantly to the last pilot and the last plane.'

I figured that Dowding was probably right. It was either that, or our superiors were so muddle-headed and incompetent that they simply didn't know what to do with us. I kept thinking about what the Corporal had said to me only a week before when I had first landed in Greece. 'This is a brand new kite,' he had said, 'and it's cost somebody *thousands* of hours to build it. And now those silly sods behind their desks in Cairo 'ave sent it out 'ere where it ain't goin' to last two minutes!' It had lasted more than that, but I couldn't see how it was going to last much longer.

We sat up on our rocky ridge beside the deep blue sea and occasionally we glanced at the burning tanker. No one had got out of her alive, but there were a number of charred corpses floating in the water. Either the current or the tide was bringing the corpses slowly towards the shore and every half hour or so I looked over my shoulder to see how close they were getting. There were about nine of them and by eleven o'clock they were only fifty yards from the rocks below us.

Somewhere around midday a large black motor-car came creeping on to our landing field. All of us became suddenly very alert. The car crept slowly over the field as though searching for something, then it turned and headed for the olive grove below us where our planes were parked. We could make out a driver at the wheel and a shadowy figure sitting in the back seat, but we couldn't see who they were or what they were wearing.

'They might be Germans with submachine-guns,' somebody said. We realized we were totally unarmed. None of us carried even a revolver.

'What make of car is it?' David asked.

We could none of us recognize the make. Someone thought it might be a Mercedes-Benz. All eyes were watching the big black motor-car.

It pulled up beside the olive grove. We sat in a close group up on our rocky ridge, alert and apprehensive. The back door opened and out stepped a formidable figure in RAF uniform. We were close enough to see him quite clearly. He had a pale orange-coloured moustache and a thick body. 'My God, it's the Air Commodore!' Dowding said, and it was. This man, who had his headquarters in Athens, had been, and indeed still was, in command of all the RAF in Greece. A few weeks ago he had directed the activities of three fighter squadrons and several bomber squadrons, but now we were all he had left. I was surprised he had managed to find out where we were.

'Where the hell is everybody?' the Air Commodore shouted.

'We're up here, sir!' we called back.

He looked up and saw us. 'Come down at once!' he shouted.

We clambered down and straggled up to him. He was standing beside the motor-car and his fierce pale-blue eyes travelled slowly over our little group. He reached into the car and brought out a thick parcel wrapped in white paper and sealed with red sealing-wax. The parcel was about the size of an average Bible, but it was floppy and bent slightly as he held it in his hands.

'This package', he said, 'must be delivered back to Elevsis at once. It is of vital importance. It must not be lost and it must not fall into enemy hands. I want a volunteer to fly there with it immediately.'

Nobody leapt forward, but that wasn't because we were afraid of returning to Elevsis. None of us was afraid of anything. We were just fed up with being pushed around.

Finally I said, 'I'll take it.' I am a compulsive volunteer. I'll say yes to anything.

'Good man,' said the Air Commodore. 'When you land, there'll be somebody waiting for you. His name is Carter. Ask him his name before you give him the package. Is that clear?'

Someone said, 'They've just been ground-strafing Elevsis again, sir. We saw them go by. One-O-Nines. Masses of them.'

'I know that,' snapped the Air Commodore. 'It makes no difference. Now you,' he said, staring at me with his fierce pale-blue eyes, 'you're to deliver this package to Carter right away and don't fail me.'

'I understand, sir,' I said.

'Carter will be the only person on the place,' the Air Commodore said. 'That is if the Germans haven't got there already. If you see any German planes on the aerodrome, for God's sake don't land. Get away at once.'

'Yes, sir,' I said. 'Where shall I go?'

'Back here. Fly straight back here. What's your name?'

'Pilot Officer Dahl, sir.'

'Very well, Dahl,' he said, weighing the package up and down in one hand. 'This is on no account to fall into enemy hands. Guard it with your life. Do I make myself clear?'

'Yes, sir,' I said, feeling important.

'Fly very low all the way,' the Air Commodore said, 'then they won't spot you. Land quickly, find Carter, give this to him and get the hell out.' He handed me the package. I wanted very much to know what was in it but I didn't dare ask.

'If you are shot down on the way, make sure you burn it,' the Air Commodore said. 'You've got a match on you, I hope?'

I stared at him. If this was the kind of genius that had been directing our operations, no wonder we were in a mess.

'Burn it,' I said. 'Very well, sir.'

Good old David Coke said, 'If he's shot down, sir, I imagine it'll burn with him.'

'Exactly,' the Air Commodore said. 'Now then, when you arrive back here, don't land. Just circle the field.' He turned to the others and said, 'The rest of you will be waiting in your cockpits, and as soon as you see him overhead, you are to taxi out and take off. You', he said, pointing at me, 'will join up with them and all of you will fly on to Argos.'

'Where's that, sir?'

'It's another fifty miles along the coast,' the Air Commodore said. 'You'll see it on your maps.'

'What happens at Argos, sir?'

'At Argos', the Air Commodore said, 'everything has been properly organized to receive you. Your ground crews are there already. So is your Squadron-Leader.'

'Is there an aerodrome at Argos, sir?' somebody asked.

'It's a landing strip,' the Air Commodore said. 'It's about a mile from the sea and our navy is standing off-shore waiting to take off the troops. Your task will be to give air cover to the navy.'

'There are only seven of us, sir,' someone said.

'You'll be doing a vital job,' the Air Commodore announced, his moustache bristling. 'You will be responsible for the protection of half the Mediterranean fleet.'

God help them, I thought.

The Air Commodore pointed a finger at me. 'You,' he said, 'get cracking! Deliver that parcel and get back here as fast as you can!'

'Yes, sir,' I said. I went over to my Hurricane and got in and did up my straps. I put the mysterious package on my lap. On the floor of the cockpit under my legs I had the paper-bag with my belongings, as well as my Log Book. My camera, I remember clearly, was hanging by its strap from my neck. I taxied out and took off. I flew very low and fast, and in eight minutes I had reached Elevsis airfield. I circled the field once, looking for Germans or their planes. The place seemed totally deserted. I glanced at the windsock and banked straight in to land against the wind.

Just as I came to the end of my landing run, I heard the air-raid sirens wailing somewhere in the distance. I jumped out of my plane with my precious package and lay down in the ditch that surrounded the field. A great swarm of Stuka dive-bombers came over with their escort of fighters above them, and I watched them as they flew on to Piraeus harbour. At Piraeus they began dive-bombing the ships.

I got back into my Hurricane and taxied up to the Operations Hut. The small buildings were splattered with bullet marks and the glass in all the windows was shattered. Several of the huts were smouldering.

I got out of my plane and walked towards the wreckage of huts. There was not a soul in sight. The entire aerodrome was deserted. In the distance I could hear the Stukas diving on to the shipping in Piraeus harbour and I could hear the bombs exploding.

'Is there anybody here?' I called out.

I felt very lonely. It was like being the only man on the moon. I stood between the Ops Hut and another small wooden hut alongside. The small hut had grey-blue smoke coming out of its shattered windows. I held the famous package tightly in my right hand.

'Hello?' I called out. 'Is there anybody here?'

Again the silence. Then a figure shimmered into sight beside one of the huts. He was a small middle-aged man wearing a pale-grey suit and he had a trilby hat on his head. He looked absurd standing there in his immaculate clothes amidst all that wreckage.

'I believe that parcel is for me,' he said.

'What is your name?' I asked him.

'Carter,' he said.

'Take it,' I said. 'By the way, what's in it?'

'Thank you for coming,' he said, smiling slightly.

I took an instant liking to Mr Carter. I knew very well he was going to stay behind when the Germans took over. He was going underground. And then he would probably be caught and tortured and shot through the head.

'Will you be all right?' I said to him. I had to raise my voice to make it heard over the crash of bombs falling on Piraeus harbour.

He reached out and shook my hand. 'Please leave at once,' he said. 'Your machine is rather conspicuous out there.'

I returned to the Hurricane and started the engine. From my cockpit I glanced back to where Mr Carter had been standing. I wanted to wave him goodbye, but he had disappeared. I opened the throttle and took off straight from where I was parked. I flew back fast and low to the field at Megara where the other six were waiting for me on the ground with their engines running. When they saw me overhead, they took off one by one and we all joined up in loose formation and flew on to look for this place that was called Argos.

The Air Commodore had said it was a landing strip. It was in fact the narrowest, bumpiest, shortest little strip of grass any of us had ever been asked to land a plane upon. But we had to get down, so down we went.

It was now about noon. The Argos landing strip was surrounded by those ever-present olive trees and in among the trees we could see that a whole lot of tents had been put up. Nothing stands out from the air more than a bunch of tents, even when they are tucked away among the olive trees. Oh brother, I thought. How long will it take them to find us here? A few hours at the most. No one should have put up any tents. The ground-crews should have slept under the trees. So should we. Our Squadron-Leader had his own tent and we found him sitting in it behind a trestle table. 'Here we are,' we said.

'Good,' he said. 'You'll be doing a patrol over the fleet this evening.'

We stood there looking at the Squadron-Leader as he sat behind his trestle table that had no papers on it.

There is something wrong about this, I told myself. There is no way in the world the Germans are going to allow us to operate our seven aircraft from this place. Our superiors were evidently expecting the worst because deep slit-trenches had been dug amongst the olive trees. But you cannot hide aeroplanes in slit-trenches and you cannot hide tents anywhere, especially tents that are a brilliant shining white.

'How long will it take them to find us here, sir?' I remember asking.

The Squadron-Leader passed a hand over his eyes, then rubbed his eye-sockets with his knuckles. 'Who knows?' he said.

'They'll wipe us out by tomorrow,' I said, greatly daring.

'We can't run away and leave the army with no air cover,' the Squadron-Leader said. 'We must do our best.'

We all trooped out of the tent feeling not very happy about anything.

The Argos Fiasco

When we left the Squadron-Leader's tent, David and I wandered off together to have a look around the camp. What we were really searching for was something to eat. We had been up since four-thirty that morning and it was now about two in the afternoon. None of us pilots had had anything at all to eat or drink since the night before. We were famished and very thirsty.

There must have been twenty-five tents scattered around that olive grove, but David and I soon located the mess tent. In the rush to move out of Elevsis during the night, it seemed that somebody had forgotten to bring the food. The local Greeks very quickly got wise to this state of affairs and they were now streaming into the camp bearing vast quantities of black olives and bottles of retsina wine. David and I bought a bucket of olives and two bottles of wine and found a shady patch of grass under a tree where we could sit down to eat and drink. We chose a spot right between our two Hurricanes so that we could keep an eye on them all the time. The number of Greek villagers mooching around was amazing. We must have been the first operational military airfield in history that was open to the public.

So we sat there, the two of us, in the shade of an olive tree on a lovely warm April afternoon, eating the small black juicy olives and drinking the retsina out of the

189

bottles. From where we sat we could see the whole of Argos Bay, but there was no sign of an evacuation fleet nor of the Royal Navy. There was just one fairly large cargo vessel lying out in the bay and there was a plume of grey smoke rising from her forward hold. We were told that she was yet another fully-laden ammunition ship and that the Germans had been over and bombed her that morning. There was now a fire below decks and everyone was waiting for the enormous explosion.

'Well, here we are,' David said, 'sitting in the sun and drinking pine juice and what a terrific cock-up it all is.'

I said, 'The Germans know very well that there are seven Hurricanes left in Greece. They intend to find us and they intend to wipe us out. Then they will have the sky all to themselves.'

'Exactly,' David said. 'And they're going to find us very quickly.'

'When they do, this camp will be an inferno,' I said.

'I shall be in the nearest slit-trench,' David said.

It was curiously peaceful sitting there chewing the delicious slightly bitter black olives and spitting out the stones and taking gulps of retsina in between. I kept looking at the ammunition ship out in the bay and waiting for her to blow up.

'I don't see any army getting into any ships,' David said. 'Who are we going to patrol over this evening?'

'Tell me seriously,' I said, 'do you think we'll come out of here alive?'

'No,' David said. 'I think we'll be dead within twenty-four hours. We'll either cop it in the air or they'll get us right here on the ground. They've got enough planes to totally *annihilate* us.'

We were still sitting in the same place at 4.30 p.m. when there was a sudden roar overhead and a single Messerschmitt 110 swept in low over our camp. The One-One-O, as we called it, was a fast twin-engined fighter with a crew of two and with a longer range than the single-engined 109. We stood up to watch him as he banked round over the water of the bay and came back again straight towards us, still flying low. He showed utter contempt for our defences because he knew we had none, and as he flashed over the second time, we could see both the pilot and the rear-gunner peering down at us with their cockpit hoods wide open. A fighter pilot never expects to come face to face with an enemy flier. To him the *machine* is the enemy. But now it was only the humans that I saw. All of a sudden those two Germans were so close they made my skin prickle. I saw their pale faces turned towards me, each face framed in a black helmet with the goggles pushed up high over the forehead, and for one thousandth of a second I fancied that my eyes looked into the eyes of the pilot.

That pilot made three workmanlike passes over our camp, then he flew off to the north.

'That's it!' David Coke said. 'That's done it!'

Men were standing up all over the camp. They were discussing the consequences of the 110's visit. It hadn't taken the Germans long to find us.

David and I knew exactly what the sequence of events would be from now on. 'We can work it out,' I said. 'It'll take him roughly half an hour to get back to his base and report our precise whereabouts. It'll take his squadron another half hour to get ready for take-off. Then another half hour for the whole lot of them to arrive back here and knock the daylights out of us. We can expect to be ground-strafed by a squadron of One-One-Os in an hour and a half's time, at six o'clock this evening.'

'We could jump them,' David said. 'If the seven of us are all airborne and waiting for them directly overhead at six o'clock we could jump them beautifully.'

The Adjutant came up to us. 'CO's orders,' he said. 'All seven of you to patrol over the fleet for as long as you can this evening. Take-off is at six o'clock sharp.'

'*Six o'clock!*' David cried. 'But that's just when they'll be coming over.'

'Who will be coming over?' the Adjutant asked.

'A squadron of One-One-Os,' David said. 'We've worked it all out. They'll be coming over to strafe us at six o'clock.'

'You seem to have better information than your commanding officer,' the Adjutant said.

We tried to explain exactly how we thought things were going to happen, but it was no good. 'Just stick to your orders,' the Adjutant said. 'Our job is to give cover to the ships evacuating our army.'

'What ships?' David said. 'And what army?'

I was only a very junior Pilot Officer, but I was damned if I was going to leave it like that. 'Look,' I said, 'will you please try to get permission for us to take off at say half-past five or even a quarter to six instead of six o'clock. It might make all the difference.'

'I can try,' the Adjutant said and he went away. He was not a bad fellow.

He returned five minutes later and shook his head. 'It's still six o'clock,' he said.

'And precisely where *are* all these ships that we are meant to be protecting?' I asked.

'Between you and me,' the Adjutant said, 'they don't actually seem to know. You'd better just fly out to sea and try to find them.'

When he had gone, I said, 'I know darn well what I'm going to do. At five fifty-five I'm going to be sitting in my cockpit at the end of the landing strip with my engine running, waiting for the signal. Then I'll be off like a dingbat.'

'I'll be right behind you,' David said. 'I think we'll be lucky if we get away before they arrive.'

At five minutes to six I was in position at the end of the strip with my engine running, ready for take-off. David was to one side, all set to follow me. The Ops Officer stood on the ground nearby looking at his watch. The five other pilots were beginning to taxi their planes out of the olive trees.

At six o'clock, the Ops Officer raised his arm and I opened the throttle. In ten seconds I was airborne and heading for the sea. I glanced round and saw David not far behind me. He caught up with me and settled in just behind my starboard wing. After a minute or so, I looked round, expecting to see the other five Hurricanes coming up to join us. They weren't there. I saw David looking over his shoulder. Then he looked across at me and shook his head. We couldn't speak to each other because our radios didn't work. But we had to obey orders so we continued flying out over the sea. We gave the smoking ammunition ship a wide berth in case it blew up beneath us and we flew on, searching for the Royal Navy.

We stayed up there for over an hour but during all that time we saw not a single ship. We learnt later that the main evacuation was taking place from the beaches of Kalamata, many miles further to the west, where our navy was getting a terrible bombing from the Ju 88s and the Stukas. But nobody had told us. We were on our way back and were just coming into the Bay of Argos again when I spotted something. It was a plane, a smallish twin-engined plane flying towards Argos and hugging the mountains of the coast.

Ha! I thought. A German shufti kite reconnoitring the area. It had to be a German. There were no other aircraft in Greece now except for our Hurricanes, and it wasn't one of those. I'll have him, I told myself. I switched my firing-button from 'safe' to 'on' and flicked on my reflector-sight. Then I opened the throttle and dived flat out for the smallish twin-engined plane. The next thing I saw was David's Hurricane rushing right up alongside me, dangerously close, and he was waggling his wings at me furiously and waving a hand from the cockpit and shaking his helmeted head from side to side. He kept pointing at the plane I was about to attack. I looked at it again. Oh, my God, it had RAF markings on its body! In five more seconds I'd have shot it down! But what on earth was a little unarmed non-combatant plane doing over here in the battle zone? I could see now that it was a de Havilland Rapide, a passenger aircraft that could carry about a dozen people. We let it go and headed back towards our landing field.

We were still several miles away when we saw the smoke. Some of it was black and some was grey and it lay like a thick blanket over the landing strip and the olive grove. I trembled to think what we would discover down there when we landed, if indeed it were possible to land through all that smoke.

We circled round and round the blanket of smoke, hoping it would clear away. There was no wind at all. I could just make out the big rock that marked the beginning of the landing strip but the rest was hidden. My fuel gauge was registering nil so it was now or never. It was the same with David. He went in first and I lost sight of him in the smoke. I waited for sixty seconds, then went in after him. It was no joke trying to land a Hurricane on a small narrow strip of grass through thick smoke, but with the big rock to guide me I managed to touch down in more or less the right place. After that, as the plane ran over the ground at eighty miles an hour, then seventy, then sixty, I shut my eyes and prayed that I wouldn't crash into David or into anything else ahead.

I didn't. I came to a stop and climbed out of the plane right away. 'David!' I called. 'Are you all right?' I couldn't see five yards in front of me.

'I'm here!' he called back. 'I'm getting out!'

Together we groped our way back into camp. There was a certain amount of chaos around the place, but to our

Argos

astonishment the ground was not littered with bloody corpses. In fact there were remarkably few casualties. What had happened was this. I had taken off at precisely six o'clock. David had followed me at one minute past six. Then three others had managed to get away, making it five altogether. But as the sixth Hurricane was gathering speed for lift-off, a swarm of Messerschmitts had come swooping in over the olive trees. The pilot who was taking off was shot down and killed. The seventh pilot had leapt out of his plane and dived into a slit-trench. So had everybody else in the camp. And there they all had crouched while the Messerschmitts swooped back and forth methodically shooting up everything they could see, the planes, the

A Hurricane, Argos

tents, the refuelling tanker, the ammunition store, the buckets of olives and the bottles of retsina.

All this was more than forty years ago, but even at that distance there seems little doubt that all seven of us should have been sent up well before six o'clock and ordered to patrol, not over a non-existent evacuation fleet, but over the landing ground itself. Then there would have been a grand battle. We might, of course, have lost more planes that way, but we would certainly have been waiting for them and we could have jumped them out of the sun with plenty of height advantage. We might even have got the lot of them. On the other hand, it is easy to be critical of one's commanders after the event and it is a game that all junior ranks enjoy playing. It is wrong to indulge in it too much.

David and I picked our way into the smoking camp. Somebody, I think it was the Adjutant, was shouting, 'All pilots this way! Hurry up! Hurry up!'

We went towards the voice and we found the Adjutant and we also found grouped around him quite an assortment of pilots who seemed to have trickled into the camp from heaven knows where. There were the six of us who were the survivors of our own squadron, but there were at least eight or ten other faces I had never seen before. An open truck was pulling through the smoke. It stopped alongside us, and then the Adjutant proceeded to read out the names of what turned out to be the five most senior pilots in the group. David and I, of course, were not among them.

'You five', the Adjutant said, 'will fly the five remaining Hurricanes to Crete immediately. All the other pilots, *and only pilots*, are to get into this truck. There is a small aircraft waiting in a field near here to fly you out of the country at once. You are to take nothing with you except your Log Books.'

We raced away to fetch our Log Books from our tents. I looked for my precious camera. It was gone. It had almost certainly been taken by one of the many Greeks wandering round the camp while I was up in the air. I couldn't really blame him, whoever he was. Now he would be able to sell the good Zeiss product back to the Germans when they arrived. But I found two exposed rolls of film and stuffed them into my trouser pocket. I grabbed my Log Book and ran outside with the other pilots and clambered into the truck. We were then driven out of the camp along a rutted dirt road to a smallish field. On the field stood the little de Havilland Rapide that I had nearly shot down thirty minutes before. We piled into the aircraft. I could see now why the Adjutant had forbidden us to bring anything with us other than our Log Books. The field wasn't more than 200 yards long and as the pilot opened his throttles and began his take-off, we none of us thought he was going to make it. Every extra pound of weight in that aeroplane would have narrowed his chances. We bounced over a stone wall at the far end of the field and watched breathlessly as the plane staggered into the air. We just made it. Everyone cheered.

I had a window-seat and David was beside me. Only twenty minutes ago we had been in among the smoking olive trees and the burnt-out tents. Now we were 1,000 feet up over the Mediterranean and flying towards the North African coast. The sun was going down and the sea below us was turning from pale green to dark blue.

'We'll have to do a night landing,' I said.

'That will be nothing for this pilot,' David said. 'If he could take off from a piddling little field like that with all of us on board, he can do anything.'

We landed two hours later on a moonlit patch of sand known as Martin Bagush in the Western Desert of Libya. In the dark we found a truck which was going back to Alexandria through the night and all of us pilots got into it. We arrived in Alexandria early the next morning filthy, unshaven and with nothing to carry except our Log Books. We had no Egyptian money. I led the lot of them, nine young pilots in all, through the streets of Alexandria to the marvellous mansion that was owned by Major Bobby Peel and his wife. They were the wealthy English couple who had put me up during my convalescence a few weeks before. I rang the doorbell. The Sudanese butler answered it. He stared in alarm at the bedraggled group of young men standing on the doorstep.

'Hello, Saleh,' I said. 'Are Major and Mrs Peel in?'

He went on staring. 'Oh sir!' he cried. 'It's you! Yes, sir, Major and Mrs Peel are having breakfast.'

I walked into the house and called out to my friends in the dining-room. The Peels were wonderful. The whole house was put at our disposal. There were bathrooms on all four floors and we swarmed into them. Razors and shaving soap and towels appeared from nowhere. All of us bathed and shaved and then sat down around the huge dining-table to a sumptuous breakfast and told the Peels about Greece.

'I don't think anyone else is going to get out,' Bobby Peel said. He was a middle-aged man too old for service, but he had a high-powered job somewhere in military headquarters. 'The navy is trying to rescue as many of our troops as they can,' he said, 'but they are having a bad time of it. They have no air cover at all.'

'You can say that again,' David Coke said.

'The whole thing was a cock-up,' someone said.

'I think it was,' Bobby Peel said. 'We should never have gone into Greece at all.'

Alexandria
15 May 1941

Dear Mama,

Well, I don't know what news I can give you. We really had the hell of a time in Greece. It wasn't much fun taking on half the German Airforce with literally a handfull of fighters. My machine was shot up quite a bit but I always managed to get back. The difficulty was to choose a time to land when the German fighters weren't ground straffing our aerodrome. Later on we hopped from place to place trying to cover the evacuation – hiding our planes in olive groves and covering them with olive branches in a fairly fruitless endeavour to prevent them being spotted by one or other of the swarms of aircraft overhead. Anyway I don't think anything as bad as that will happen again . . .

The Grecian episode was a very small part of the war that was raging all over the world, but so far as the Middle

East was concerned, it was an important one. The troops and planes that were lost in that abortive campaign had all been drawn from our already overstretched forces in the Western Desert, and as a result those forces were now diminished to such an extent that for the next two years our desert army suffered defeat after defeat and Rommel was at one time actually threatening to capture Egypt and the whole of the Middle East. It took two years to rebuild the Desert Army to a point where the Battle of Alamein could be won and the Middle East secured for the rest of the war.

The handful of pilots who survived the Grecian campaign were tremendously lucky. The odds were strongly against any of us coming out alive. The five who flew our remaining Hurricanes to Crete were to fight valiantly on the island when the Germans attacked a short time later with a massive airborne invasion. I know that one of them at least, Bill Vale from 80 Squadron, survived and escaped when the island was captured, and lived to fight again, but I do not know what happened to the others.

Palestine and Syria

After they had taken Greece in May 1941, the Germans mounted a massive airborne invasion of Crete. They captured Crete and they also took the island of Rhodes, and after that, flushed with success, they turned their eyes towards the softest spots in all of the Middle East – Syria and the Lebanon. These spots were soft because they were controlled totally by a large and very efficient pro-German Vichy French army.

Most people know about the very great trouble the Vichy French fleet gave to Britain in 1941 after France had fallen. Our navy actually had to put the French warships out of action by bombarding them at Oran to make sure they didn't fall into German hands. Most people know about that. But not many know about the chaos the Vichy French caused at the same time in Syria and the Lebanon. They were fanatically anti-British and pro-German, and if the Germans with their help had managed to get a foothold in Syria at that particular moment, they could have marched down into Egypt by the back door. The Vichy French had therefore to be dislodged from Syria as soon as possible.

The Syrian Campaign, as it was called, started up almost immediately after Greece, and a very considerable army composed of British and Australian troops was sent up through Palestine to fight the disgusting pro-Nazi

Frenchmen. This small war was a bloody affair in which thousands of lives were lost, and I for one have never forgiven the Vichy French for the unnecessary slaughter they caused.

Air cover for our army and navy in this campaign was to be provided by the remnants of good old 80 Squadron, and about a dozen new Hurricanes were speedily brought out from England to replace the ones lost in Greece. I began to see now why it had been important to get us pilots out of the Grecian mess alive, even without our planes. It takes longer to train a pilot than it does to build an aeroplane. Mind you, it would have made even more sense to have saved some of those Grecian Hurricanes as well as the pilots, but that didn't happen.

Eighty Squadron were to assemble at Haifa in northern Palestine in the last week of May 1941. Each pilot was told to collect his new Hurricane at Abu Suweir on the Suez Canal and fly it to Haifa aerodrome. I asked Middle East Fighter Command if someone else could fly my plane to Haifa for me because I wanted to drive myself up there in my own motor-car. I had become the very proud possessor of a nine-year-old 1932 Morris Oxford saloon, a machine whose body had been sprayed with a noxious brown paint the colour of canine faeces, and whose maximum speed on a straight and level track was thirty-five miles per hour. With some reluctance Fighter Command granted my request.

There was a ferry across the Suez Canal at Ismailia. It was simply a wooden float that was pulled from one bank to the other by wires, and I drove the car on to it and was taken to the Sinai bank. But before I was allowed to start the long and lonely journey across the Sinai Desert, I had to show the officials that I had with me five gallons of spare petrol and a five-gallon can of drinking water. Then off I went.

I loved that journey. I loved it, I think, because I had never before in my life been totally without sight of another human being for a full day and a night. Few people have. There was a single narrow strip of hard road running through the soft sands of the desert all the way from the Canal up to Beersheba on the Palestine border. The total distance across the desert was about 200 miles and there was not a village or a hut or a shack or any sign of human life over the entire distance. As I went chugging along through this sterile and treeless wasteland, I began to wonder how many hours or days I would have to wait for another traveller to turn up if my old car should break down.

I was soon to find out. I had been going for some five hours when my radiator began to boil over in the fierce afternoon heat. I stopped and opened the bonnet and waited for everything to cool down. After an hour or so I was able to remove the radiator cap and pour in some more water, but I realized that it would be pointless to drive on again in the full heat of the sun because the engine would simply boil over once more. I must wait, I told myself, until the sun had gone down. But there again I knew I must not drive at night because my headlights did not work and I was certainly not going to run the risk of sliding off the narrow hard strip in the dark and getting bogged down in soft sand. It was a bit of a dilemma and the only way out of it that I could see would be to wait until dawn and make a dash for Beersheba before the sun began to roast my engine again.

I had brought a large water-melon with me as emergency rations, and now I cut a chunk out of it and flipped away the black seeds with the point of my knife and ate the lovely cool pink flesh standing beside the car in the sun. There was no shade anywhere except inside the car, but in there it was like an oven. I longed for a parasol or anything else that would give me a little shade, but I had nothing. I was wearing khaki shorts and a khaki shirt and I had a blue RAF cap on my head. I found a rag and soaked it in the tepid drinking water and draped it over my head and put the cap over it. That helped. I walked slowly up and down the boiling hot strip of road and kept gazing in absolute wonder at the amazing landscape that surrounded me. There was the blazing sun, the vast hot sky, and beneath it all on every side a great pale sea of yellow sand that was not quite of this world. There were mountains now in the distance on the right-hand side of the road, pale Tanagra-coloured mountains faintly glazed with blue that rose up suddenly out of the desert and faded away in a haze of heat against the sky. The stillness was overpowering. There was no sound at all, no voice of bird or insect anywhere, and it gave me a queer godlike feeling to be standing there alone in such a splendid hot inhuman landscape – as though I were on another planet, on Jupiter or Mars, or in some place more desolate still, where never would the grass grow green nor a rose bloom red.

I kept pacing slowly up and down the road, waiting for the sun to go down and for the cool night to come along. Then suddenly, in the sand just a foot or so off the road, I saw a giant scorpion. Jet black she was and fully six inches long, and clinging to her back, like passengers on the top of an open bus, were her babies. I bent a little closer to count them. One, two, three, four, five ... there were fourteen of them altogether! At that point she saw me. I am quite sure I was the first human she had ever seen in her life, and she curled her tail up high over her body with the pincers wide open, ready to strike in defence of her family. I stepped back a pace but continued to watch her, fascinated. She scuttled over the sand and disappeared into a hole that was her burrow.

When the sun went down, it became dark almost at once, and with the night came a blessed and dramatic drop in temperature. I ate another hunk of water-melon, drank some water and then curled up as best I could in the back seat of the car and went to sleep.

I started off again the next morning at first light, and in another couple of hours I had crossed the desert and come to Beersheba. I drove on northwards across Palestine, through Jerusalem and Nazareth, and in the late afternoon I skirted Mount Carmel and dropped down into the town of Haifa. The aerodrome was outside the town on the edge of the sea, and I drove my old car in triumph past the guard at the gates and parked it alongside the officers' mess, which was a small hut made of wood and corrugated iron.

We had nine Hurricanes at Haifa and the same number

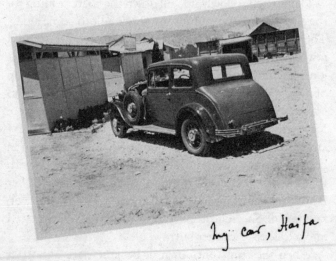

My car, Haifa

of pilots, and in the days that followed we were kept very busy. Our main job was to protect the navy. Our navy had two large cruisers and several destroyers stationed in Haifa harbour and every day they would sail up the coast past Tyre and Sidon to bombard the Vichy French forces in the mountains around the Damour river. And whenever our ships came out, the Germans came over to bomb them. They came from Rhodes, where they had built up a strong force of Junkers Ju 88s, and just about every day we met those Ju 88s over the fleet. They came over at 8,000 feet and we were usually waiting for them. We would dive in amongst them, shooting at their engines and getting shot at by their front- and rear-gunners, and the sky was filled with bursting shells from the ships below and when

Crashed Vichy French plane, Haifa

one of them exploded close to you it made your plane jump like a stung horse. Sometimes the Vichy French air force joined up with the Germans. They had American Glenn Martins and French Dewoitines and Potez 63s, and we shot some of them down and they killed four of our nine pilots. And then the Germans hit the destroyer *Isis* and we spent the whole day circling above her in relays and fighting off the Ju 88s while a naval tug towed her back to Haifa.

Once we went out to ground-strafe some Vichy French planes on an airfield near Rayak and as we swept in surprise low over the field at midday we saw to our astonishment a bunch of girls in brightly coloured cotton dresses standing out by the planes with glasses in their hands having drinks with the French pilots, and I remember seeing bottles of wine standing on the wing of one of the planes as we went swooshing over. It was a Sunday morning and the Frenchmen were evidently entertaining their girlfriends and showing off their aircraft to them, which was a very French thing to do in the middle of a war at a front-line aerodrome. Every one of us held our fire on that first pass over the flying field and it was wonderfully comical to see the girls all dropping their wine glasses and galloping in their high heels for the door of the nearest building. We went round again, but this time we were no longer a surprise and they were ready for us with their ground defences, and I am afraid that our chivalry resulted in damage to several of our Hurricanes, including my own. But we destroyed five of their planes on the ground.

One morning at Haifa the Squadron-Leader called me aside and told me that a small satellite landing field had been prepared about thirty miles inland behind Mount Carmel from which the Squadron could operate should our aerodrome at Haifa be bombed out. 'I want you to fly over there and have a look at it,' the Squadron-Leader said. 'Don't land unless it seems safe and if you do land I want to know what it's like. It's meant to serve as a small secret hideaway where those Ju 88s could never find us.'

I flew off alone and in ten minutes I spotted a ribbon of dry earth that had been rolled out in the middle of a large field of sweet-corn. To one side was a plantation of fig trees and I could see several wooden huts among the trees. I made a landing, pulled up and switched off the engine.

my Hurricane, Haifa

Suddenly from out of the fig trees and out of the huts burst a stream of children. They surrounded my Hurricane, jumping about with excitement and shouting and laughing and pointing. There must have been forty or fifty of them altogether. Then out came a tall bearded man who strode among the children and ordered them to stand away from the plane. I climbed out of the cockpit and the man came forward and shook my hand. 'Welcome to our little settlement,' he said, speaking with a strong German accent.

I had seen enough English-speaking Germans in Dar es Salaam to know the accent well, and now, quite naturally, anyone who had anything even remotely Germanic about him set alarm-bells ringing in my head. What is more, this place, according to the Squadron-Leader, was meant to be secret and here I was being met by a welcoming committee of fifty screaming children and a huge man with a black beard who looked like the Prophet Isaiah and spoke like a parody of Hitler. I began to wonder whether I had come to the right spot.

'I didn't think anyone knew about this,' I said to the bearded man.

The man smiled. 'We cut down the corn ourselves and helped to roll out the strip,' he said. 'This is our cornfield.'

'But who are you and who are all these children?' I asked him.

'We are Jewish refugees,' he said. 'The children are all orphans. This is our home.' The man's eyes were startlingly bright. The black pupil in the centre of each of them seemed larger and blacker and brighter than any I had ever seen and the iris surrounding each pupil was brilliant blue.

In their excitement at seeing a real live fighter plane, the children were beginning to press right up against the aircraft, reaching out and making the elevators in the tail-plane move up and down. 'No, no!' I cried out. 'Please don't do that! Please keep away! You could damage it!'

The man spoke sharply to the children in German and they all fell back.

'Refugees from where?' I asked him. 'And how did you get here?'

'Would you like a cup of coffee?' he said. 'Let's go into my hut.' He picked out three of the older boys and set them to guard the Hurricane. 'Your plane will be quite safe now,' he said.

I followed him into a small wooden hut standing among fig trees. There was a dark-haired young woman inside and the man spoke to her in German but he did not introduce me. The woman poured some water from a bucket into a saucepan and lit a paraffin burner and proceeded to heat water for coffee. The man and I sat down on stools at a plain table. There was a loaf of what looked like home-baked bread on the table, and a knife.

'You seem surprised to find us here,' the man said.

'I am,' I said. 'I wasn't expecting to find anyone.'

'We are everywhere,' the man said. 'We are all over the country.'

'Forgive me,' I said, 'but I don't understand. Who do you mean by we?'

'Jewish refugees.'

I really didn't know what he was talking about. I had been living in East Africa for the past two years and in those times the British colonies were parochial and isolated. The local newspaper, which was all we got to read, had not mentioned anything about Hitler's persecution of the Jews in 1938 and 1939. Nor did I have the faintest idea that the greatest mass murder in the history of the world was actually taking place in Germany at that moment.

'Is this your land?' I asked him.

'Not yet,' he said.

'You mean you are hoping to buy it?'

He looked at me in silence for a while. Then he said, 'The land is at present owned by a Palestinian farmer but he has given us permission to live here. He has also allowed us some fields so that we can grow our own food.'

'So where do you go from here?' I asked him. 'You and all your orphans?'

'We don't go anywhere,' he said, smiling through his black beard. 'We stay here.'

'Then you will all become Palestinians,' I said. 'Or perhaps you are that already.'

He smiled again, presumably at the naïvety of my questions.

'No,' the man said, 'I do not think we will become Palestinians.'

'Then what will you do?'

'You are a young man who is flying aeroplanes,' he said, 'and I do not expect you to understand our problems.'

'What problems?' I asked him. The young woman put two mugs of coffee on the table as well as a tin of condensed milk that had two holes punctured in the top. The man dripped some milk from the tin into my mug and stirred it for me with the only spoon. He did the same for his own coffee and then took a sip.

'You have a country to live in and it is called England,' he said. 'Therefore you have no problems.'

'No problems!' I cried. 'England is fighting for her life all by herself against virtually the whole of Europe! We're even fighting the Vichy French and that's why we're in Palestine right now! Oh, we've got problems all right!' I was getting rather worked up. I resented the fact that this man sitting in his fig grove said that I had no problems when I was getting shot at every day. 'I've got problems myself', I said, 'in just trying to stay alive.'

'That is a very small problem,' the man said. 'Ours is much bigger.'

I was flabbergasted by what he was saying. He didn't seem to care one bit about the war we were fighting. He appeared to be totally absorbed in something he called 'his problem' and I couldn't for the life of me make it out. 'Don't you care whether we beat Hitler or not?' I asked him.

'Of course I care. It is essential that Hitler be defeated. But that is only a matter of months and years. Historically, it will be a very short battle. Also it happens to be England's battle. It is not mine. My battle is one that has been going on since the time of Christ.'

'I am not with you at all,' I said. I was beginning to wonder whether he was some sort of a nut. He seemed to have a war of his own going on which was quite different to ours.

I still have a very clear picture of the inside of that hut and of the bearded man with the bright fiery eyes who kept talking to me in riddles. 'We need a homeland,' the man was saying. 'We need a country of our own. Even the Zulus have Zululand. But we have nothing.'

'You mean the Jews have no country?'

'That's exactly what I mean,' he said. 'It's time we had one.'

'But how in the world are you going to get yourselves a country?' I asked him. 'They are all occupied. Norway belongs to the Norwegians and Nicaragua belongs to the Nicaraguans. It's the same all over.'

'We shall see,' the man said, sipping his coffee. The

dark-haired woman was washing up some plates in a basin of water on another small table and she had her back to us.

'You could have Germany,' I said brightly. 'When we have beaten Hitler then perhaps England would give you Germany.'

'We don't want Germany,' the man said.

'Then which country did you have in mind?' I asked him, displaying more ignorance than ever.

'If you want something badly enough,' he said, 'and if you *need* something badly enough, you can always get it.' He stood up and slapped me on the back. 'You have a lot to learn,' he said. 'But you are a good boy. You are fighting for freedom. So am I.'

He led me out of the hut and through the grove of fig

Ramat David

trees that were covered with small unripe fruit, and all the children were still clustered around my Hurricane, gazing at it in absolute wonder. I had bought another Zeiss camera in Cairo to replace the one lost in Greece, and I stopped and took a quick photograph of some of the children around the plane. The bearded man gently made a path through the throng of youngsters, tousling the hair of several of them in an affectionate way as he went by and smiling at them all. Then he shook my hand once again and said, 'Do not think we are not grateful. You are doing a fine job. I wish you luck.'

'You too,' I said and I climbed into the cockpit and started the engine. I flew back to Haifa and reported that the landing strip seemed quite serviceable and that there were lots of children for the pilots to play with should we

80 Squadron camp, Ramat David

Ramat David

ever have to go there. Three days later, the Ju 88s began bombing Haifa in earnest so we flew our Hurricanes out to the cornfield and a large tent was put up in the fig grove for us to live in. We were only there for a few days and we got on fine with the children, but the tall bearded man, when confronted with so many of us, seemed to close up completely and became very distant. He never spoke intimately to me again as he had done on our first meeting, nor did he have much to say to anyone else.

The name of that tiny settlement of Jewish orphans was Ramat David. It is written in my Log Book. Whether or not anything exists on the site today I do not know. The only name close to it I can find in my atlas is Ramat Dawid, but that is not the same place. It is too far south.

Home

I had been at Haifa for exactly four weeks, flying intensively every day (my Log Book records that on 15 June I went up five times and was in the air for a total of eight hours and ten minutes), when suddenly I began to get the most blinding headaches. I got them only when I was flying and then only when dog-fighting with the enemy. The pain would hit me when I was doing very steep turns and making sudden changes of direction, when the body was subjected to high gravitational stresses, and the agony when it came was like a knife in the forehead. Several times it caused me to black out for seconds on end. I reported this to the squadron doctor. He examined my medical records and gravely shook his head. My condition he said, was without question due to the severe head injuries I had received when my Gladiator crashed in the Western Desert, and I must on no account fly a fighter plane again. He said that if I did, I might well lose consciousness altogether while up in the air and that would be the end of both me and the plane I was flying.

'What happens now?' I asked the doctor.

'You will be invalided home to Britain,' he said. 'You are no use to us out here any longer.'

I packed my kit-bag and said goodbye to my gallant friend David Coke. He would stay with the squadron after this Syrian Campaign was over. He would continue flying his Hurricane for many months in the Western Desert against the Germans. He would be decorated for bravery. And then at long last, tragically but almost inevitably, he would be shot down and killed.

Haifa, Palestine
28 June 1941

Dear Mama,

   We've been doing some pretty intensive flying just lately – you may have heard about it a little on the wireless. Sometimes I've been doing as much as 7 hours a day, which is a lot in a fighter. Anyway, my head didn't take it any too well, and for the last 3 days I've been off flying. I may have to have another medical board & see if I'm really fit to fly out here. They may even send me to England, which wouldn't be a bad thing, would it. It's a pity in a way though, because I've just got going. I've got 5 confirmed, four Germans and one French, and quite a few unconfirmed – and lots on the ground from groundstraffing landing grounds. We've lost 4 pilots killed in the Squadron in the last 2 weeks, shot down by the French. Otherwise this country is great fun and definitely flowing with milk and honey . . .

I drove my old Morris Oxford back to Egypt and this time the weather was cooler when I came to the Sinai Desert. I made the crossing in seven hours, with only one stop in order to pour more petrol into the tank. Not long after that I embarked at Suez on the great French trans-atlantic luxury liner *Ile de France*, which had been converted into a troop-ship. We sailed south to Durban and there I was transferred to another troop-ship whose name I have

POST OFFICE TELEGRAM

Charges to pay
RECEIVED

No.

OFFICE STAMP

Prefix. Time handed in. Office of Origin and Service Instructions. Words. 113 To.

C. 13.05 19. ALEXANDRIA

From

N.L.C. DAHL

COMING HOME VERY SOON BY SEA.
VERY FIT. SYRIAN WAR FUN. CABLE BY RETURN
ANY PARTICULAR MATERIALS OR ANYTHING YOU
WANT. ALSO SIZES SILK STOCKINGS ALL SIX OF
YOU. EVERYTHING HERE ADDRESS CABLE CARE PEEL
ALEXANDRIA. LOVE. RONALD DAHL.

For free repetition of doubtful words telephone "TELEGRAMS ENQUIRY" or call, with this form
at office of delivery. Other enquiries should be accompanied by this form and, if possible, the envelope.

Delivered 3 months late!

forgotten. On her, we called in at Cape Town, then we went northwards to Freetown in Sierra Leone. I went ashore at Freetown and bought quite literally a sackful of lemons and limes to take home to my family in war-rationed England. I filled another sack with things like tinned marmalade and sugar and chocolate, all of which I knew were virtually unobtainable at home. In a small shop in Freetown I found lengths of superb pre-war French silks and I bought enough of those to make a dress for each of my sisters.

The journey from Freetown to Liverpool was a hazardous affair. Our convoy was continually attacked by packs of U-boats and also by the long-range German Focke-Wulf bombers flying out of western France, and all the service-men on board were detailed to man machine-guns and Bofors guns which had been scattered in great numbers over the upper decks. We used to bang away at the massive Focke-Wulfs as they swept low overhead, and now and again, when we thought we saw a periscope in the waves we banged away at that, too. Every day for two weeks I thought our ship was going to be finished off either by bombs or by torpedoes. We saw three other ships in the convoy going down and once we stopped to pick up survivors and once we had a near-miss from a bomb which sprayed our entire vessel with water and soaked us all.

But our luck held, and after two more weeks at sea, on a black wet night in early autumn, we nosed our way into Liverpool Docks and tied up. I ran down the gangway immediately and went off to try and find a telephone kiosk that had not been bombed out of action. When I found one at last, I was literally shaking with excitement at the thought of speaking to my mother again after three years. She could not possibly have known that I was on my way home. The censor would not have allowed such things to be written in letters, and I myself had not heard from anyone in the family for many months. No letter from England had found its way up to Haifa. I got the trunk-call operator and asked for our old number in Kent. After a pause, she told me it had been disconnected months ago. I asked her to consult Directory Inquiries. No, she said, there were no Dahls in Bexley or anywhere else in Kent come to that.

The operator sounded like a lovely elderly lady. I told

her how I had been abroad for three years and was trying to find my mother. 'She'll have moved,' the operator said. 'She'll probably have been bombed out like all the rest of them and she's had to move somewhere else.' She was too kind to add that the whole family might well have been killed in the bombing, but I knew what she was thinking and she probably guessed that I was thinking it, too.

I waited in the pitch-dark telephone kiosk down in the docks of Liverpool, pressing the receiver hard to my ear and wondering what I was going to say to my mother if I was lucky enough to get through. After a while the operator came back on the line and said, 'I have found one Mrs Dahl. She's a Mrs S. Dahl and she's at a place called Grendon Underwood. Could that be the one?'

'Oh no,' I said, 'I don't think that could be her. But thank you so much for trying.' What I should have said was, 'Try it, we might be lucky,' because that, as it turned out, was my mother's new home. A bomb had landed in their house in Kent while my mother and two of my sisters and their four dogs were sensibly sheltering in the cellar. They had scrambled out the next morning and having seen their house in ruins had simply got into the small family Hillman Minx, the three of them and the four dogs, and had driven through London north into the Buckinghamshire countryside. Then they had cruised slowly through the small villages looking for a house that had a *For Sale* notice by the front gate. In the tiny rural village of Grendon Underwood, ten miles north of Aylesbury, they found a small white cottage with a thatched roof and it had the notice-board they were looking for stuck in the hedge. My mother had no money with which to buy it, but one of the sisters had some savings and she bought the place on the spot and they all moved in. I knew none of this on that dark wet evening in Liverpool docks.

I went back to the ship and collected my kit-bag and my two sacks of lemons and limes and tinned marmalade, and I staggered to the station with this load on my back and found a train for London. I sat all of the next morning by the window of the train gazing in wonder at the green, rain-sodden fields of England. I had forgotten what they looked like. After the dusty plains of East Africa and the sandy deserts of Egypt they looked ridiculously and unnaturally green.

My train did not reach London until nightfall. At Euston Station I shouldered my belongings and trudged through the blacked-out bomb-shattered streets, heading for the West End. When I got to Leicester Square, I somehow managed to find in the darkness a small seedy hotel. I went in and asked the manageress if I could use the telephone. An RAF uniform with wings on the jacket was a great passport to have in England in 1941. The Battle of Britain had been won by the fighters and now the bombers were beginning seriously to attack Germany. The manageress looked at my wings and said that of course I could use her telephone.

With the London telephone directory in my hands, I had a bright idea. I looked up the name of my ancient half-sister who I knew was married to a biochemist called Professor A. A. Miles (the Goat's Tobacco man in *Boy*).

They lived in London. I found their number and rang it. The ancient half-sister answered the phone and I told her it was me. When the squeals of surprise had died down, I asked her where my mother and my other sisters were. They were in Buckinghamshire, she told me. She would telephone my mother at once to give her the amazing news.

'Don't do that,' I said. 'Just give me the number. I'll call her myself.'

The half-sister gave me the number and I wrote it down. She also told me she could give me a bed for the night and I wrote down her address in Hampstead. 'Try to get a taxi,' she said. 'If you don't have any money, we can pay for it when you arrive.' I said I would do that.

Then I rang my mother.

'Hello,' I said. 'Is that you, mama?'

She knew my voice at once. There was a brief silence on the line as she struggled to get control of her emotions. I had been away for three years and we had not spoken in that time. In those days you did not telephone to one another from far-away countries as you do today. And three years is a long time to wait for the return of an only son who is flying fighters in places like the Western Desert and Greece. Eight months ago she had seen the village postman standing at the door of the cottage holding a buff-coloured telegram envelope in his hand. Every wife and every mother in the country lived in dread of opening the front door to a postman with a telegram. Many of them refused even to slit the envelope. They could not bear to read the terse War Office message: *We regret to inform you of the death of your husband [or son] killed in action etc. etc.* They would leave the telegram on the dresser until someone else came along to open it for them. My mother had put her telegram aside and had waited for one of her daughters to return from her daily stint of driving a lorry. Then they had both sat down on the sofa and my sister had opened the envelope and unfolded the piece of paper inside. REGRET TO ADVISE YOU, the message read, YOUR SON WOUNDED AND IN HOSPITAL IN ALEXANDRIA. The relief was unbearable.

'I'd like a drink,' my mother had said.

The sister had got out the precious, impossible-to-buy bottle from the cupboard and they had both had a good stiff slug of neat gin there and then.

'Is that really you, Roald?' my mother's voice was saying now very softly on the telephone.

'I'm back,' I said.

'Are you all right?'

'I'm fine,' I said.

There was another pause, and I heard her whispering urgently to one of the sisters who must have been standing beside her.

'When will we see you?' she asked.

'Tomorrow,' I said. 'As soon as I can get a train. I've got some lemons for you, and some limes, and some big tins of marmalade.' I didn't know what else to say.

'Try to get an early train.'

'Yes,' I said. 'I'll get a train as early as I can.'

I thanked the manageress who had been listening from behind her little desk in the hotel lobby, and I went out to try and find a taxi. I was standing just inside the porch of the hotel in Leicester Square in the pitch darkness of the black-out when a group of four or five soldiers peered into the porch. 'It's a bloody officer!' one shouted. 'Let's 'ave 'im!'

The leering slightly drunken faces closed in on me and the fists were coming when one of them called out suddenly, 'Hey stop! 'Ee's RAF! 'Ee's a pilot! 'Ee's got ruddy wings on 'im!' They backed away and disappeared into the darkness.

It shook me a bit to realize that this was a posse of drunken soldiers prowling around the black streets of London searching for an officer to beat up.

No taxi came, so I slung my enormously heavy kit-bags over my shoulders and set out to walk to Hampstead. From Leicester Square that is a long walk even *without* three kit-bags to carry, but I was young and strong and I was on my way home and I felt I could have walked a hundred miles had it been necessary.

It took me an hour and three-quarters to reach the ancient half-sister's house, and there was a happy meeting and I gave presents of lemons and limes and marmalade and then fell gratefully into bed.

Early the next morning, I was driven to Marylebone Station and found a train for Aylesbury. The journey took an hour and fifteen minutes. At Aylesbury I found a bus which, so the driver assured me, would go right through the village of Grendon Underwood. The bus took longer than the train, and all the way I kept asking an old man who sat beside me to be sure to tell me when we were approaching Grendon Underwood.

'We're coming into it now,' he said at last. 'It's not much of a place. Just a few cottages and a pub.'

I caught sight of my mother when the bus was still a hundred yards away. She was standing patiently outside the gate of the cottage waiting for the bus to come along, and for all I knew she had been standing there when the earlier bus had gone by an hour or two before. But what is one hour or even three hours when you have been waiting three years?

I signalled the bus-driver and he stopped the bus for me right outside the cottage, and I flew down the steps of the bus straight into the arms of the waiting mother.

Mama's Cottage

Only This

First published in *Ladies' Home Journal*
(September 1944)

That night the frost was very heavy. It covered the hedges and whitened the grass in the fields so that it seemed almost as though it had been snowing. But the night was clear and beautiful and bright with stars, and the moon was nearly full.

The cottage stood alone in a corner of the big field. There was a path from the front door which led across the field to a stile and on over the next field to a gate which opened on to the lane about three miles from the village. There were no other houses in sight and the country around was open and flat and many of the fields were under the plough because of the war.

The light of the moon shone upon the cottage. It shone through the open window into the bedroom where the woman was asleep. She slept lying on her back, with her face upturned to the ceiling, with her long hair spread out around her on the pillow, and although she was asleep, her face was not the face of someone who is resting. Once she had been beautiful, but now there were thin furrows running across her forehead and there was a tightness about the way in which her skin was stretched over the cheekbones. But her mouth was still gentle, and as she slept, she did not close her lips.

The bedroom was small, with a low ceiling, and for furniture there was a dressing-table and an armchair. The clothes of the woman lay over the back of the armchair where she had put them when she undressed. Her black shoes were on the floor beside the chair. On the dressing-table there was a hairbrush, a letter and a large photograph of a young boy in uniform who wore a pair of wings on the left side of his tunic. It was a smiling photograph, the kind that one likes to send to one's mother, and it had a thin, black frame made of wood. The moon shone through the open window and the woman slept her restless sleep. There was no noise anywhere save for the soft, regular noise of her breathing and the rustle of the bedclothes as she stirred in her sleep.

Then, from far away, there came a deep, gentle rumble which grew and grew and became louder and louder until soon the whole sky seemed to be filled with a great noise which throbbed and throbbed and kept on throbbing and did not stop.

Right at the beginning, even before it came close, the woman had heard the noise. In her sleep she had been waiting for it, listening for the noise and dreading the moment when it would come. When she heard it, she opened her eyes and for a while she lay quite still, listening. Then she sat up, pushed the bedclothes aside and got out of bed. She went over to the window and placing her hands on the window sill, she leaned out, looking up into the sky; and her long hair fell down over her shoulders, over the thin cotton nightdress which she wore. For many minutes she stood there in the cold, leaning out of the window, hearing the noise, looking up and searching the sky; but she saw only the bright moon and the stars.

'God keep you,' she said aloud. 'Oh dear God keep you safe.'

Then she turned and went quickly over to the bed, pulled the blankets away and wrapped them round her shoulders like a shawl. She slipped her bare feet into the black shoes and walked over to the armchair and pushed it forward so that it was right up in front of the window. Then she sat down.

The noise and the throbbing overhead was very great. For a long time it continued as the huge procession of bombers moved towards the south. All the while the woman sat huddled in her blankets, looking out of the window into the sky.

Then it was over. Once more the night became silent. The frost lay heavy on the field and on the hedges and it seemed as though the whole countryside was holding its breath. An army was marching in the sky. All along the route people had heard the noise and knew what it was; they knew that soon, even before they had gone to sleep, there would be a battle. Men drinking beer in the pubs had stopped their talking in order to listen. Families in their houses had turned off the radio and gone out into their gardens, where they stood looking up into the sky. Soldiers arguing in their tents had stopped their shouting, and men and women walking home at night from the factories had stood still on the road, listening to the noise.

It is always the same. As the bombers move south

across the country at night, the people who hear them become strangely silent. For those women whose men are with the planes, the moment is not an easy one to bear.

Now they had gone, and the woman lay back in the armchair and closed her eyes, but she did not sleep. Her face was white and the skin seemed to have been drawn tightly over her cheeks and gathered up in wrinkles around her eyes. Her lips were parted and it was as though she were listening to someone talking. Almost she could hear the sound of his voice as he used to call to her from outside the window when he came back from working in the fields. She could hear him saying he was hungry and asking what there was for supper, and then when he came in he would put his arm around her shoulder and talk to her about what he had been doing all day. She would bring in the supper and he would sit down and start to eat and always he would say, Why don't you have some, and she never knew what to answer except that she wasn't hungry. She would sit and watch him and pour out his tea, and after a while she would take his plate and go out into the kitchen to get him some more.

It was not easy having only one child. The emptiness when he was not there and the knowing all the time that something might happen; the deep conscious knowing that there was nothing else to live for except this; that if something did happen, then you too would be dead. There would be no use in sweeping the floor or washing the dishes or cleaning the house; there would be no use in gathering wood for the fire or in feeding the hens; there would be no use in living.

Now, as she sat there by the open window she did not feel the cold; she felt only a great loneliness and a great fear. The fear took hold of her and grew upon her so that she could not bear it, and she got up from the chair and leaned out of the window again, looking up into the sky. And as she looked the night was no longer beautiful; it was cold and clear and immensely dangerous. She did not see the fields or the hedges or the carpet of frost upon the countryside; she saw only the depths of the sky and the danger that was there.

Slowly she turned and sank down again into her chair. Now the fear was great. She could think of nothing at all except that she must see him and be with him, that she must see him now because tomorrow would be too late. She let her head rest against the back of the chair and when she closed her eyes she saw the aircraft; she saw it clearly in the moonlight, moving forward through the night like a great, black bird. She was close to it and she could see the way in which the nose of the machine reached out far ahead of everything, as though the bird was craning its neck in the eagerness of its passage. She could see the markings on the wings and on the body and she knew that he was inside. Twice she called to him, but there was no answer; then the fear and the longing welled up within her so that she could stand it no longer and it carried her forward through the night and on and on until she was with him, beside him, so close that she could have touched him had she put out her hand.

He was sitting at the controls with gloves on his hands, dressed in a great bulky flying suit which made his body look huge and shapeless and twice its normal size. He was looking straight ahead at the instruments on the panel, concentrating upon what he was doing and thinking of nothing except flying the machine.

Now she called to him again and he heard her. He looked around and when he saw her, he smiled and stretched out a hand and touched her shoulder, and then all the fear and the loneliness and the longing went out of her and she was happy.

For a long time she stood beside him watching him as he flew the machine. Every now and then he would look around and smile at her, and once he said something, but she could not hear what it was because of the noise of the engines. Suddenly he pointed ahead through the glass windshield of the aeroplane and she saw that the sky was full of searchlights. There were many hundreds of them; long white fingers of light travelling lazily across the sky, swaying this way and that, working in unison so that sometimes several of them would come together and meet in the same spot and after a while they would separate and meet again somewhere else, all the time searching the night for the bombers which were moving in on the target.

Behind the searchlights she saw the flak. It was coming up from the town in a thick many-coloured curtain, and the flash of the shells as they burst in the sky lit up the inside of the bomber.

He was looking straight ahead now, concentrating upon the flying, weaving through the searchlights and going directly into this curtain of flak, and she watched and waited and did not dare to move or to speak lest she distract him from his task.

She knew that they had been hit when she saw the flames from the nearest engine on the left side. She watched them through the glass of the side panel, licking against the surface of the wing as the wind blew them backwards, and she watched them take hold of the wing and come dancing over the black surface until they were right up under the cockpit itself. At first she was not frightened. She could see him sitting there, very cool, glancing continually to one side, watching the flames and flying the machine, and once he looked quickly around and smiled at her and she knew then that there was no danger. All around she saw the searchlights and the flak and the explosions of the flak and the colours of the tracer, and the sky was not a sky but just a small confined space which was so full of lights and explosions that it did not seem possible that one could fly through it.

But the flames were brighter now on the left wing. They had spread over the whole surface. They were alive and active, feeding on the fabric, leaning backwards in the wind which fanned them and encouraged them and gave them no chance of going out.

Then came the explosion. There was a blinding white flash and a hollow *crumph* as though someone had burst a blown-up paper bag; then there was nothing but flames and thick whitish-grey smoke. The flames were coming up through the floor and through the sides of the cockpit; the smoke was so thick that it was difficult to see and almost impossible to breathe. She became terrified and panicky because he was still sitting there at the controls, flying the machine, fighting to keep it on an even keel, turning the wheel first to one side, then to the other, and suddenly there was a blast of cold air and she had a vague impression of urgent crouching figures scrambling past her and throwing themselves away from the burning aircraft.

Now the whole thing was a mass of flames and through the smoke she could see him still sitting there, fighting with the wheel while the crew got out, and as he did so he held one arm up over his face because the heat was so great. She rushed forward and took him by the shoulders and shook him and shouted, 'Come on, quickly, you must get out, quickly, quickly.'

Then she saw that his head had fallen forward upon his chest and that he was limp and unconscious. Frantically she tried to pull him out of the seat and towards the door, but he was too limp and heavy. The smoke was filling her lungs and her throat so that she began to retch and gasp for breath. She was hysterical now, fighting against death and against everything, and she managed to get her hands under his arms and drag him a little way towards the door. But it was impossible to get him farther. His legs were tangled around the wheel and there was a buckle some-where which she could not undo. She knew then that it was impossible, that there was no hope because of the smoke and the fire and because there was no time; and suddenly all the strength drained out of her body. She fell down on top of him and began to cry as she had never cried before.

Then came the spin and the fierce rushing dive downwards and she was thrown forward into the fire so that the last she knew was the bright yellow of the flames and the smell of the burning.

Her eyes were closed and her head was resting against the back of the chair. Her hands were clutching the edges of the blankets as though she were trying to pull them tighter around her body and her long hair fell down over her shoulders.

Outside the moon was low in the sky. The frost lay heavier than ever on the fields and on the hedges and there was no noise anywhere. Then from far away in the south came a deep gentle rumble which grew and grew and became louder and louder until soon the whole sky was filled with the noise and the singing of those who were coming back.

But the woman who sat by the window never moved. She had been dead for some time.

Yesterday Was Beautiful

First published in *Over to You* (1945)

He bent down and rubbed his ankle where it had been sprained with the walking so that he couldn't see the ankle bone. Then he straightened up and looked around him. He felt in his pocket for a packet of cigarettes, took one out and lit it. He wiped the sweat from his forehead with the back of his hand and he stood in the middle of the street looking around him.

'Dammit, there must be someone here,' he said aloud, and he felt better when he heard the sound of his voice.

He walked on, limping, walking on the toe of his injured foot, and when he turned the next corner he saw the sea and the way the road curved around between the ruined houses and went on down the hill to the edge of the water. The sea was calm and black. He could clearly make out the line of hills on the mainland in the distance and he estimated that it was about eight miles away. He bent down again to rub his ankle. 'God dammit,' he said. 'There must be some of them still alive.' But there was no noise anywhere, and there was a stillness about the buildings and about the whole village which made it seem as though the place had been dead for a thousand years.

Suddenly he heard a little noise as though someone had moved his feet on the gravel and when he looked around he saw the old man. He was sitting in the shade on a stone beside a water trough, and it seemed strange that he hadn't seen him before.

'Health to you,' said the pilot. '*Ghia sou.*'

He had learned Greek from the people up around Larissa and Yanina.

The old man looked up slowly, turning his head but not moving his shoulders. He had a greyish-white beard. He had a cloth cap on his head and he wore a shirt which had no collar. It was a grey shirt with thin black stripes. He looked at the pilot and he was like a blind man who looks towards something but does not see.

'Old man, I am glad to see you. Are there no other people in the village?'

There was no answer.

The pilot sat down on the edge of the water trough to rest his ankle.

'I am *Inglese*,' he said. 'I am an aviator who has been shot down and jumped out by the parachute. I am *Inglese*.'

The old man moved his head slowly up and down. '*Inglesus*,' he said quietly. 'You are *Inglesus*.'

'Yes, I am looking for someone who has a boat. I wish to go back to the mainland.'

There was a pause, and when he spoke, the old man seemed to be talking in his sleep. 'They come over all the time,' he said. 'The *Germanoi* they come over all the time.' The voice had no expression. He looked up into the sky, then he turned and looked behind him in the sky. 'They will come again today, *Inglese*. They will come again soon.' There was no anxiety in his voice. There was no expression whatsoever. 'I do not understand why they come to us,' he added.

The pilot said, 'Perhaps not today. It is late now. I think they have finished for today.'

'I do not understand why they come to us, *Inglese*. There is no one here.'

The pilot said, 'I am looking for a man who has a boat who can take me across to the mainland. Is there a boat owner now in the village?'

'A boat?'

'Yes.' There was a pause while the question was considered.

'There is such a man.'

'Could I find him? Where does he live?'

'There is a man in the village who owns a boat.'

'Please tell me what is his name?'

The old man looked up again at the sky. 'Joannis is the one here who has a boat.'

'Joannis who?'

'Joannis Spirakis,' and he smiled. The name seemed to have a significance for the old man and he smiled.

'Where does he live?' the pilot said. 'I am sorry to be giving you this trouble.'

'Where he lives?'

'Yes.'

The old man considered this too. Then he turned and looked down the street towards the sea. 'Joannis was living in the house nearest to the water. But his house isn't any more. The *Germanoi* hit it this morning. It was early and it was still dark. You can see the house isn't any more. It isn't any more.'

'Where is he now?'

'He is living in the house of Antonina Angelou. That house there with the red colour on the window.' He pointed down the street.

'Thank you very much. I will go and call on the boat owner.'

'Ever since he was a boy,' the old man went on, 'Joannis has had a boat. His boat is white with a blue line around the top,' and he smiled again. 'But at the moment I do not think he will be in the house. His wife will be there. Anna will be there, with Antonina Angelou. They will be home.'

'Thank you again. I will go and speak to his wife.'

The pilot got up and started to go down the street, but almost at once the man called after him, '*Inglese.*'

The pilot turned.

'When you speak to the wife of Joannis – when you speak to Anna . . . you should remember something.' He paused, searching for words. His voice wasn't expressionless any longer and he was looking up at the pilot.

'Her daughter was in the house when the *Germanoi* came. It is just something that you should remember.'

The pilot stood on the road waiting.

'Maria. Her name was Maria.'

'I will remember,' answered the pilot. 'I am sorry.'

He turned away and walked down the hill to the house with the red windows. He knocked and waited. He knocked again louder and waited. There was the noise of footsteps and the door opened.

It was dark in the house and all he could see was that the woman had black hair and that her eyes were black like her hair. She looked at the pilot who was standing out in the sunshine.

'Health to you,' he said. 'I am *Inglese*.'

She did not move.

'I am looking for Joannis Spirakis. They say that he owns a boat.'

Still she did not move.

'Is he in the house?'

'No.'

'Perhaps his wife is here. She could know where he is.'

At first there was no answer. Then the woman stepped back and held open the door. 'Come in, *Inglesus*,' she said.

He followed her down the passage and into a back room. The room was dark because there was no glass in the windows – only patches of cardboard. But he could see the old woman who was sitting on the bench with her arms resting on the table. She was tiny. She was small like a child and her face was like a little screwed-up ball of brown paper.

'Who is it?' she said in a high voice.

The first woman said, 'This is an *Inglesus*. He is looking for your husband because he requires a boat.'

'Health to you, *Inglesus*,' the old woman said.

The pilot stood by the door, just inside the room. The first woman stood by the window and her arms hung down by her sides.

The old woman said, 'Where are the *Germanoi*?' Her voice seemed bigger than her body.

'Now they are around Lamia.'

'Lamia.' She nodded. 'Soon they will be here. Perhaps

tomorrow they will be here. But I do not care. Do you hear me, *Inglesus*, I do not care.' She was leaning forward a little in her chair and the pitch of her voice was becoming higher. 'When they come it will be nothing new. They have already been here. Every day they have been here. Every day they come over and they bom bom bom and you shut your eyes and you open them again and you get up and you go outside and the houses are just dust – and the people.' Her voice rose and fell.

She paused, breathing quickly, then she spoke more quietly. 'How many have you killed, *Inglesus*?'

The pilot put out a hand and leaned against the door to rest his ankle.

'I have killed some,' he said quietly.

'How many?'

'As many as I could, old woman. We cannot count the number of men.'

'Kill them all,' she said softly. 'Go and kill every man and every woman and every baby. Do you hear me, *Inglesus*? You must kill them all.' The little brown ball of paper became smaller and more screwed up. 'The first one I see I shall kill.' She paused. 'And then, *Inglesus*, and then later, his family will hear that he is dead.'

The pilot did not say anything. She looked up at him and her voice was different. 'What is it you want, *Inglesus*?'

He said, 'About the *Germanoi*, I am sorry. But there is not much we can do.'

'No,' she answered, 'there is nothing. And you?'

'I am looking for Joannis. I wish to use his boat.'

'Joannis,' she said quietly, 'he is not here. He is out.'

Suddenly she pushed back the bench, got to her feet and went out of the room. 'Come,' she said. He followed her down the passage towards the front door. She looked even smaller when she was standing than when she was sitting down and she walked quickly down the passage towards the door and opened it. She stepped out into the sunshine and for the first time he saw how very old she was.

She had no lips. Her mouth was just wrinkled skin like the rest of her face and she screwed up her eyes at the sun and looked up the road.

'There he is,' she said. 'That's him.' She pointed at the old man who was sitting beside the drinking trough.

The pilot looked at the man. Then he turned to speak to the old woman, but she had disappeared into the house.

A Piece of Cake

Revised and retitled version of 'Shot Down over Libya',
published in *Over to You* (1945)

I do not remember much of it; not beforehand anyway;
not until it happened.

There was the landing at Fouka, where the Blenheim
boys were helpful and gave us tea while we were being
refuelled. I remember the quietness of the Blenheim boys,
how they came into the mess-tent to get some tea and sat
down to drink it without saying anything; how they got
up and went out when they had finished drinking and still
they did not say anything. And I knew that each one was
holding himself together because the going was not very
good right then. They were having to go out too often,
and there were no replacements coming along.

We thanked them for the tea and went out to see if
they had finished refuelling our Gladiators. I remember
that there was a wind blowing which made the windsock
stand out straight, like a signpost, and the sand was
blowing up around our legs and making a rustling noise
as it swished against the tents, and the tents flapped in the
wind so that they were like canvas men clapping their
hands.

'Bomber boys unhappy,' Peter said.

'Not unhappy,' I answered.

'Well, they're browned off.'

'No. They've had it, that's all. But they'll keep going. You can see they're trying to keep going.'

Our two old Gladiators were standing beside each other in the sand and the airmen in their khaki shirts and shorts seemed still to be busy with the refuelling. I was wearing a thin white cotton flying suit and Peter had on a blue one. It wasn't necessary to fly with anything warmer.

Peter said, 'How far away is it?'

'Twenty-one miles beyond Charing Cross,' I answered, 'on the right side of the road.' Charing Cross was where the desert road branched north to Mersah Matruh. The Italian Army was outside Mersah, and they were doing pretty well. It was about the only time, so far as I know, that the Italians have done pretty well. Their morale goes up and down like a sensitive altimeter, and right then it was at forty thousand because the Axis was on top of the world. We hung around waiting for the refuelling to finish.

Peter said, 'It's a piece of cake.'

'Yes. It ought to be easy.'

We separated and I climbed into my cockpit. I have always remembered the face of the airman who helped me to strap in. He was oldish, about forty, and bald except for a neat patch of golden hair at the back of his head. His face was all wrinkles, his eyes were like my grandmother's eyes, and he looked as though he had spent his life helping to strap in pilots who never came back. He stood on the wing pulling my straps and said, 'Be careful. There isn't any sense not being careful.'

'Piece of cake,' I said.

'Like hell.'

'Really. It isn't anything at all. It's a piece of cake.'

I don't remember much about the next bit; I only remember about later on. I suppose we took off from Fouka and flew west towards Mersah, and I suppose we flew at about eight hundred feet. I suppose we saw the sea to starboard, and I suppose – no, I am certain – that it was blue and that it was beautiful, especially where it rolled up on to the sand and made a long thick white line east and west as far as you could see. I suppose we flew over Charing Cross and flew on for twenty-one miles to where they had said it would be, but I do not know. I know only that there was trouble, lots and lots of trouble, and I know that we had turned round and were coming back when the trouble got worse. The biggest trouble of all was that I was too low to bale out, and it is from that point on that my memory comes back to me. I remember the dipping of the nose of the aircraft and I remember looking down the nose of the machine at the ground and seeing a little clump of camel-thorn growing there all by itself. I remember seeing some rocks lying in the sand beside the camel-thorn, and the camel-thorn and the sand and the rocks leaped out of the ground and came to me. I remember that very clearly.

Then there was a small gap of not-remembering. It might have been one second or it might have been thirty; I do not know. I have an idea that it was very short, a second perhaps, and next I heard a *crumph* on the right as the starboard wing tank caught fire, then another *crumph* on the left as the port tank did the same. To me that was not

247

significant, and for a while I sat still, feeling comfortable, but a little drowsy. I couldn't see with my eyes, but that was not significant either. There was nothing to worry about. Nothing at all. Not until I felt the hotness around my legs. At first it was only a warmness and that was all right too, but all at once it was a hotness, a very stinging scorching hotness up and down the sides of each leg.

I knew that the hotness was unpleasant, but that was all I knew. I disliked it, so I curled my legs up under the seat and waited. I think there was something wrong with the telegraph system between the body and the brain. It did not seem to be working very well. Somehow it was a bit slow in telling the brain all about it and in asking for instructions. But I believe a message eventually got through, saying, 'Down here there is a great hotness. What shall we do? (Signed) Left Leg and Right Leg.' For a long time there was no reply. The brain was figuring the matter out.

Then slowly, word by word, the answer was tapped over the wires. 'The – plane – is – burning. Get – out – repeat – get – out – get – out.' The order was relayed to the whole system, to all the muscles in the legs, arms and body, and the muscles went to work. They tried their best; they pushed a little and pulled a little, and they strained greatly, but it wasn't any good. Up went another telegram, 'Can't get out. Something holding us in.' The answer to this one took even longer in arriving, so I just sat there waiting for it to come, and all the time the hotness increased. Something was holding me down and it was up to the brain to find out what it was. Was it giants' hands pressing on my shoulders, or heavy stones or houses or steam rollers or filing cabinets or gravity or was it ropes? Wait a minute. Ropes – ropes. The message was beginning to come through. It came very slowly. 'Your – straps. Undo – your – straps.' My arms received the message and went to work. They tugged at the straps, but they wouldn't undo. They tugged again and again, a little feebly, but as hard as they could, and it wasn't any use. Back went the message, 'How do we undo the straps?'

This time I think that I sat there for three or four minutes waiting for the answer. It wasn't any use hurrying or getting impatient. That was the one thing of which I was sure. But what a long time it was all taking. I said aloud, 'Bugger it. I'm going to be burned. I'm . . .' but I was interrupted. The answer was coming – no, it wasn't – yes, it was, it was slowly coming through. 'Pull – out – the – quick – release – pin – you – bloody – fool – and – hurry.'

Out came the pin and the straps were loosed. Now, let's get out. Let's get out, let's get out. But I couldn't do it. I simply couldn't lift myself out of the cockpit. Arms and legs tried their best but it wasn't any use. A last desperate message was flashed upwards and this time it was marked 'Urgent'.

'Something else is holding us down,' it said. 'Something else, something else, something heavy.'

Still the arms and legs did not fight. They seemed to know instinctively that there was no point in using up their strength. They stayed quiet and waited for the answer, and oh what a time it took. Twenty, thirty, forty hot seconds. None of them really white-hot yet, no sizzling of flesh or smell of burning meat, but that would come any moment now, because those old Gladiators aren't made of stressed steel like a Hurricane or a Spit.

They have taut canvas wings, covered with magnificently inflammable dope, and underneath there are hundreds of small thin sticks, the kind you put under the logs for kindling, only these are drier and thinner. If a clever man said, 'I am going to build a big thing that will burn better and quicker than anything else in the world,' and if he applied himself diligently to his task, he would probably finish up by building something very like a Gladiator. I sat still waiting.

Then suddenly the reply, beautiful in its briefness, but at the same time explaining everything. 'Your – parachute – turn – the – buckle.'

I turned the buckle, released the parachute harness and with some effort hoisted myself up and tumbled over the side of the cockpit. Something seemed to be burning, so I rolled about a bit in the sand, then crawled away from the fire on all fours and lay down.

I heard some of my machine-gun ammunition going off in the heat and I heard some of the bullets thumping into the sand near by. I did not worry about them; I merely heard them.

Things were beginning to hurt. My face hurt most. There was something wrong with my face. Something had happened to it. Slowly I put up a hand to feel it. It was sticky. My nose didn't seem to be there. I tried to feel my teeth, but I cannot remember whether I came to any conclusion about them. I think I dozed off.

All of a sudden there was Peter. I heard his voice and

I heard him dancing around and yelling like a madman and shaking my hand and saying, 'Jesus, I thought you were still inside. I came down half a mile away and ran like hell. Are you all right?'

I said, 'Peter, what has happened to my nose?'

I heard him striking a match in the dark. The night comes quickly in the desert. There was a pause.

'It actually doesn't seem to be there very much,' he said. 'Does it hurt?'

'Don't be a bloody fool, of course it hurts.'

He said he was going back to his machine to get some morphia out of his emergency pack, but he came back again soon, saying he couldn't find his aircraft in the dark.

'Peter,' I said, 'I can't see anything.'

'It's night,' he answered. 'I can't see either.'

It was cold now. It was bitter cold, and Peter lay down close alongside so that we could both keep a little warmer. Every now and then he would say, 'I've never seen a man without a nose before.' I kept spewing a lot of blood and every time I did it, Peter lit a match. Once he gave me a cigarette, but it got wet and I didn't want it anyway.

I do not know how long we stayed there and I remember only very little more. I remember that I kept telling Peter that there was a tin of sore-throat tablets in my pocket, and that he should take one, otherwise he would catch my sore throat. I remember asking him where we were and him saying, 'We're between the two armies,' and then I remember English voices from an English patrol asking if we were Italians. Peter said something to them; I cannot remember what he said.

Later I remember hot thick soup and one spoonful making me sick. And all the time the pleasant feeling that Peter was around, being wonderful, doing wonderful things and never going away. That is all that I can remember.

The men stood beside the aeroplane painting away and talking about the heat.

'Painting pictures on the aircraft,' I said.

'Yes,' said Peter. 'It's a great idea. It's subtle.'

'Why?' I said. 'Just you tell me.'

'They're funny pictures,' he said. 'The German pilots will all laugh when they see them; they'll shake so with their laughing that they won't be able to shoot straight.'

'Oh baloney, baloney, baloney.'

'No, it's a great idea. It's fine. Come and have a look.'

We ran towards the line of aircraft. 'Hop, skip, jump,' said Peter. 'Hop, skip, jump, keep in time.'

'Hop, skip, jump,' I said. 'Hop, skip, jump,' and we danced along.

The painter on the first aeroplane had a straw hat on his head and a sad face. He was copying the drawing out of a magazine, and when Peter saw it he said, 'Boy oh boy look at that picture,' and he began to laugh. His laugh began with a rumble and grew quickly into a belly-roar and he slapped his thighs with his hands both at the same time and went on laughing with his body doubled up and his mouth wide open and his eyes shut. His silk top hat fell off his head on to the sand.

'That's not funny,' I said.

'Not funny!' he cried. 'What d'you mean, "not funny"?'

Look at me. Look at me laughing. Laughing like this I couldn't hit anything. I couldn't hit a hay wagon or a house or a louse.' And he capered about on the sand, gurgling and shaking with laughter. Then he seized me by the arm and we danced over to the next aeroplane. 'Hop, skip, jump,' he said. 'Hop, skip, jump.'

There was a small man with a crumpled face writing a long story on the fuselage with a red crayon. His straw hat was perched right on the back of his head and his face was shiny with sweat.

'Good morning,' he said. 'Good morning, good morning,' and he swept his hat off his head in a very elegant way.

Peter said, 'Shut up,' and bent down and began to read what the little man had been writing. All the time Peter was spluttering and rumbling with laughter, and as he read he began to laugh afresh. He rocked from one side to the other and danced around on the sand slapping his thighs with his hands and bending his body. 'Oh my, what a story, what a story, what a story. Look at me. Look at me laughing,' and he hopped about on his toes, shaking his head and chortling like a madman. Then suddenly I saw the joke and I began to laugh with him. I laughed so much that my stomach hurt and I fell down and rolled around on the sand and roared and roared because it was so funny that there was nothing else I could do.

'Peter, you're marvellous,' I shouted. 'But can all those German pilots read English?'

'Oh hell,' he said. 'Oh hell. Stop,' he shouted. 'Stop your work,' and the painters all stopped their painting and turned round slowly and looked at Peter. They did a little caper on their toes and began to chant in unison. 'Rubbishy things – on all the wings, on all the wings, on all the wings,' they chanted.

'Shut up,' said Peter. 'We're in a jam. We must keep calm. Where's my top hat?'

'What?' I said.

'You can speak German,' he said. 'You must translate for us. He will translate for you,' he shouted to the painters. 'He will translate.'

Then I saw his black top hat lying in the sand. I looked away, then I looked around and saw it again. It was a silk opera hat and it was lying there on its side in the sand.

'You're mad,' I shouted. 'You're madder than hell. You don't know what you're doing. You'll get us all killed. You're absolutely plumb crazy, do you know that? You're crazier than hell. My God, you're crazy.'

'Goodness, what a noise you're making. You mustn't shout like that; it's not good for you.' This was a woman's voice. 'You've made yourself all hot,' she said, and I felt someone wiping my forehead with a handkerchief. 'You mustn't work yourself up like that.'

Then she was gone and I saw only the sky, which was pale blue. There were no clouds and all around were the German fighters. They were above, below and on every side and there was no way I could go; there was nothing I could do. They took it in turns to come in to attack and they flew their aircraft carelessly, banking and looping and dancing in the air. But I was not frightened, because of the funny pictures on my wings. I was confident and I thought, I am going to fight a hundred of them alone and I'll shoot them all down. I'll shoot them while they are laughing; that's what I'll do.

Then they flew closer. The whole sky was full of them. There were so many that I did not know which ones to watch and which ones to attack. There were so many that they made a black curtain over the sky and only here and there could I see a little of the blue showing through. But there was enough to patch a Dutchman's trousers, which was all that mattered. So long as there was enough to do that, then everything was all right.

Still they flew closer. They came nearer and nearer, right up in front of my face so that I saw only the black crosses which stood out brightly against the colour of the Messerschmitts and against the blue of the sky; and as I turned my head quickly from one side to the other I saw more aircraft and more crosses and then I saw nothing but the arms of the crosses and the blue of the sky. The arms had hands and they joined together and made a circle and danced around my Gladiator, while the engines of the Messerschmitts sang joyfully in a deep voice. They were playing Oranges and Lemons and every now and then two would detach themselves and come out into the middle of the floor and make an attack and I knew then that it was Oranges and Lemons. They banked and swerved and danced upon their toes and they leaned against the air first to one side, then to the other. 'Oranges and lemons said the bells of St Clements,' sang the engines.

But I was still confident. I could dance better than they and I had a better partner. She was the most beautiful girl in the world. I looked down and saw the curve of her neck and the gentle slope of her pale shoulders and I saw her slender arms, eager and outstretched.

Suddenly I saw some bullet-holes in my starboard wing and I got angry and scared both at the same time; but mostly I got angry. Then I got confident and I said, 'The German who did that had no sense of humour. There's always one man in a party who has no sense of humour. But there's nothing to worry about; there's nothing at all to worry about.'

Then I saw more bullet-holes and I got scared. I slid back the hood of the cockpit and stood up and shouted, 'You fools, look at the funny pictures. Look at the one on my tail; look at the story on my fuselage. Please look at the story on my fuselage.'

But they kept on coming. They tripped into the middle of the floor in twos, shooting at me as they came. And the engines of the Messerschmitts sang loudly. 'When will you pay me, said the bells of Old Bailey?' sang the engines, and as they sang the black crosses danced and swayed to the rhythm of the music. There were more holes in my wings, in the engine cowling and in the cockpit.

Then suddenly there were some in my body.

But there was no pain, even when I went into a spin, when the wings of my plane went flip flip, flip flip, faster and faster, when the blue sky and the black sea chased each other round and round until there was no longer any sky or sea but just the flashing of the sun as I turned. But the black crosses were following me down, still dancing and still holding hands and I could still hear the singing of their engines. 'Here comes a candle to light you to bed, here comes a chopper to chop off your head,' sang the engines.

Still the wings went flip flip, flip flip, and there was neither sky nor sea around me, but only the sun.

Then there was only the sea. I could see it below me and I could see the white horses, and I said to myself, Those are white horses riding a rough sea. I knew then that my brain was going well because of the white horses and because of the sea. I knew that there was not much time because the sea and the white horses were nearer, the white horses were bigger and the sea was like a sea and like water, not like a smooth plate. Then there was only one white horse, rushing forward madly with his bit in his teeth, foaming at the mouth, scattering the spray with his hooves and arching his neck as he ran. He galloped on madly over the sea, riderless and uncontrollable, and I could tell that we were going to crash.

After that it was warmer, and there were no black crosses and there was no sky. But it was only warm because it was not hot and it was not cold. I was sitting in a great red chair made of velvet and it was evening. There was a wind blowing from behind.

'Where am I?' I said.

'You are missing. You are missing, believed killed.'

'Then I must tell my mother.'

'You can't. You can't use that phone.'

'Why not?'

'It goes only to God.'

'What did you say I was?'

'Missing, believed killed.'

'That's not true. It's a lie. It's a lousy lie because here I am and I'm not missing. You're just trying to frighten me and you won't succeed. You won't succeed, I tell you, because I know it's a lie and I'm going back to my squadron. You can't stop me because I'll just go. I'm going, you see, I'm going.'

I got up from the red chair and began to run.

'Let me see those X-rays again, Nurse.'

'They're here, Doctor.' This was the woman's voice again, and now it came closer. 'You have been making a noise tonight, haven't you? Let me straighten your pillow for you, you're pushing it on to the floor.' The voice was close and it was very soft and nice.

'Am I missing?'

'No, of course not. You're fine.'

'They said I was missing.'

'Don't be silly; you're fine.'

Oh everyone's silly, silly, silly, but it was a lovely day, and I did not want to run but I couldn't stop. I kept on running across the grass and I couldn't stop because my legs were carrying me and I had no control over them. It was as if they did not belong to me, although when I looked down I saw that they were mine, that the shoes on the feet were mine and that the legs were joined to my body. But they would not do what I wanted; they just went on running across the field and I had to go with them. I ran and ran and ran, and although in some places the field was rough and bumpy, I never stumbled. I ran past trees and hedges and in one field there were some sheep which stopped their eating and scampered off as I ran past them. Once I saw my mother in a pale-grey dress bending down picking mushrooms, and as I ran past she looked up and said, 'My basket's nearly full; shall we go home soon?' but my legs wouldn't stop and I had to go on.

Then I saw the cliff ahead and I saw how dark it was beyond the cliff. There was this great cliff and beyond it there was nothing but darkness, although the sun was shining in the field where I was running. The light of the sun stopped dead at the edge of the cliff and there was only darkness beyond. That must be where the night begins, I thought, and once more I tried to stop but it was not any good. My legs began to go faster towards the cliff and they began to take longer strides, and I reached down with my hand and tried to stop them by clutching the cloth of my trousers, but it did not work; then I tried to fall down. But my legs were nimble, and each time I threw myself I landed on my toes and went on running.

Now the cliff and the darkness were much nearer and I could see that unless I stopped quickly I should go over the edge. Once more I tried to throw myself to the ground and once more I landed on my toes and went on running.

I was going fast as I came to the edge and I went straight on over it into the darkness and began to fall.

At first it was not quite dark. I could see little trees growing out of the face of the cliff, and I grabbed at them with my hands as I went down. Several times I managed to catch hold of a branch, but it always broke off at once because I was so heavy and because I was falling so fast, and once I caught a thick branch with both hands and the tree leaned forward and I heard the snapping of the roots one by one until it came away from the cliff and I went on falling. Then it became darker because the sun and the day were in the fields far away at the top of the cliff, and as I fell I kept my eyes open and watched the darkness turn from grey-black to black, from black to jet black and from jet black to pure liquid blackness which I could touch with my hands but which I could not see. But I went on falling, and it was so black that there was nothing anywhere and it was not any use doing anything or caring or thinking because of the blackness and because of the falling. It was not any use.

'You're better this morning. You're much better.' It was the woman's voice again.

'Hallo.'

'Hallo; we thought you were never going to get conscious.'

'Where am I?'

'In Alexandria; in hospital.'

'How long have I been here?'

'Four days.'

'What time is it?'

'Seven o'clock in the morning.'

'Why can't I see?'

I heard her walking a little closer.

'Oh, we've just put a bandage around your eyes for a bit.'

'How long for?'

'Just for a while. Don't worry. You're fine. You were very lucky, you know.'

I was feeling my face with my fingers but I couldn't feel it; I could only feel something else.

'What's wrong with my face?'

I heard her coming up to the side of my bed and I felt her hand touching my shoulder.

'You mustn't talk any more. You're not allowed to talk. It's bad for you. Just lie still and don't worry. You're fine.'

I heard the sound of her footsteps as she walked across the floor and I heard her open the door and shut it again.

'Nurse,' I said. 'Nurse.'

But she was gone.

They Shall Not Grow Old

First published in *Ladies' Home Journal*
(March 1945)

The two of us sat outside the hangar on wooden boxes.

It was noon. The sun was high and the heat of the sun was like a close fire. It was hotter than hell out there by the hangar. We could feel the hot air touching the inside of our lungs when we breathed and we found it better if we almost closed our lips and breathed in quickly; it was cooler that way. The sun was upon our shoulders and upon our backs, and all the time the sweat seeped out from our skin, trickled down our necks, over our chests and down our stomachs. It collected just where our belts were tight around the tops of our trousers and it filtered under the tightness of our belts where the wet was very uncomfortable and made prickly heat on the skin.

Our two Hurricanes were standing a few yards away, each with that patient, smug look which fighter planes have when the engine is not turning, and beyond them the thin black strip of the runway sloped down towards the beaches and towards the sea. The black surface of the runway and the white grassy sand on the sides of the runway shimmered and shimmered in the sun. The heat-haze hung like a vapour over the aerodrome.

The Stag looked at his watch.

'He ought to be back,' he said.

The two of us were on readiness, sitting there for orders to take off. The Stag moved his feet on the hot ground.

'He ought to be back,' he said.

It was two and a half hours since Fin had gone and he certainly should have come back by now. I looked up into the sky and listened. There was the noise of airmen talking beside the petrol wagon and there was the faint pounding of the sea upon the beaches; but there was no sign of an aeroplane. We sat a little while longer without speaking.

'It looks as though he's had it,' I said.

'Yep,' said the Stag. 'It looks like it.'

The Stag got up and put his hands into the pockets of his khaki shorts. I got up too. We stood looking northwards into the clear sky, and we shifted our feet on the ground because of the softness of the tar and because of the heat.

'What was the name of that girl?' said the Stag, without turning his head.

'Nikki,' I answered.

The Stag sat down again on his wooden box, still with his hands in his pockets, and he looked down at the ground between his feet. The Stag was the oldest pilot in the squadron; he was twenty-seven. He had a mass of coarse ginger hair which he never brushed. His face was pale, even after all this time in the sun, and covered with freckles. His mouth was wide and tight closed. He was not tall but his shoulders under his khaki shirt were broad and thick like those of a wrestler. He was a quiet person.

'He'll probably be all right,' he said, looking up. 'And anyway, I'd like to meet the Vichy Frenchman who can get Fin.'

We were in Palestine fighting the Vichy French in Syria. We were at Haifa, and three hours before the Stag, Fin and I had gone on readiness. Fin had flown off in response to an urgent call from the Navy, who had phoned up and said that there were two French destroyers moving out of Beyrouth harbour. Please go at once and see where they are going, said the Navy. Just fly up the coast and have a look and come back quickly and tell us where they are going.

So Fin had flown off in his Hurricane. The time had gone by and he had not returned. We knew that there was no longer much hope. If he hadn't been shot down, he would have run out of petrol some time ago.

I looked down and I saw his blue RAF cap, which was lying on the ground where he had thrown it as he ran to his aircraft, and I saw the oil stains on top of the cap and the shabby bent peak. It was difficult now to believe that he had gone. He had been in Egypt, in Libya and in Greece. On the aerodrome and in the mess we had had him with us all of the time. He was gay and tall and full of laughter, this Fin, with black hair and a long straight nose which he used to stroke up and down with the tip of his finger. He had a way of listening to you while you were telling a story, leaning back in his chair with his face to the ceiling but with his eyes looking down on the ground, and it was only last night at supper that he had suddenly said, 'You know, I wouldn't mind marrying Nikki. I think she's a good girl.'

The Stag was sitting opposite him at the time, eating baked beans.

'You mean just occasionally,' he said.

Nikki was in a cabaret in Haifa.

'No,' said Fin. 'Cabaret girls make fine wives. They are never unfaithful. There is no novelty for them in being unfaithful; that would be like going back to the old job.'

The Stag had looked up from his beans. 'Don't be such a bloody fool,' he said. 'You wouldn't really marry Nikki.'

'Nikki,' said Fin with great seriousness, 'comes of a fine family. She is a good girl. She never uses a pillow when she sleeps. Do you know why she never uses a pillow when she sleeps?'

'No.'

The others at the table were listening now. Everyone was listening to Fin talking about Nikki.

'Well, when she was very young she was engaged to be married to an officer in the French Navy. She loved him greatly. Then one day when they were sunbathing together on the beach he happened to mention to her that he never used a pillow when he slept. It was just one of those little things which people say to each other for the sake of conversation. But Nikki never forgot it. From that time onwards she began to practise sleeping without a pillow. One day the French officer was run over by a truck and killed; but although to her it was very uncomfortable, she still went on sleeping without a pillow to preserve the memory of her lover.'

Fin took a mouthful of beans and chewed them slowly.

'It is a sad story,' he said. 'It shows that she is a good girl. I think I would like to marry her.'

That was what Fin had said last night at supper. Now he was gone and I wondered what little thing Nikki would do in his memory.

The sun was hot on my back and I turned instinctively in order to take the heat upon the other side of my body. As I turned, I saw Carmel and the town of Haifa. I saw the steep pale-green slope of the mountain as it dropped down towards the sea, and below it I saw the town and the bright colours of the houses shining in the sun. The houses with their whitewashed walls covered the sides of Carmel and the red roofs of the houses were like a rash on the face of the mountain.

Walking slowly towards us from the grey corrugated-iron hangar came the three men who were the next crew on readiness. They had their yellow Mae Wests slung over their shoulders and they came walking slowly towards us, holding their helmets in their hands as they came.

When they were close, the Stag said, 'Fin's had it,' and they said, 'Yes, we know.' They sat down on the wooden boxes which we had been using, and immediately the sun was upon their shoulders and upon their backs and they began to sweat. The Stag and I walked away.

The next day was a Sunday and in the morning we flew up the Lebanon valley to ground-strafe an aerodrome called Rayak. We flew past Hermon, who had a hat of snow upon his head, and we came down out of the sun on to Rayak and on to the French bombers on the aerodrome and began our strafing. I remember that as we flew past, skimming low over the ground, the doors of the French bombers opened. I remember seeing a whole lot of women in white dresses running out across the aerodrome; I remember particularly their white dresses.

You see, it was a Sunday and the French pilots had asked their ladies out from Beyrouth to look over the bombers. The Vichy pilots had said, Come out on Sunday morning and we will show you our aeroplanes. It was a very Vichy French thing for them to do.

So when we started shooting, they all tumbled out and began to run across the aerodrome in their white Sunday dresses.

I remember hearing Monkey's voice over the radio, saying, 'Give them a chance, give them a chance,' and the whole squadron wheeled around and circled the aerodrome once while the women ran over the grass in every direction. One of them stumbled and fell twice and one of them was limping and being helped by a man, but we gave them time. I remember watching the small bright flashes of a machine gun on the ground and thinking that they should at least have stopped their shooting while we were waiting for their white-dressed women to get out of the way.

That was the day after Fin had gone. The next day the Stag and I sat once more at readiness on the wooden boxes outside the hangar. Paddy, a big fair-haired boy, had taken Fin's place and was sitting with us.

It was noon. The sun was high and the heat of the sun was like a close fire. The sweat ran down our necks, down inside our shirts, over our chests and stomachs, and we sat there waiting for the time when we would be relieved. The Stag was sewing the strap on to his helmet with a needle and cotton and telling of how he had seen Nikki the night before in Haifa and of how he had told her about Fin.

Suddenly we heard the noise of an aeroplane. The Stag stopped his talking and we all looked up. The noise was coming from the north, and it grew louder and louder as the aeroplane flew closer, and then the Stag said suddenly, 'It's a Hurricane.'

The next moment it was circling the aerodrome, lowering its wheels to land.

'Who is it?' said the fair-haired Paddy. 'No one's gone out this morning.'

Then, as it glided past us on to the runway, we saw the number on the tail of the machine, H.4427, and we knew that it was Fin.

We were standing up now, watching the machine as it taxied towards us, and when it came up close and swung round for parking we saw Fin in the cockpit. He waved his hand at us, grinned and got out. We ran up and shouted at him, 'Where've you been?' 'Where in the hell have you been?' 'Did you force-land and get away again?' 'Did you find a woman in Beyrouth?' 'Fin, where in the hell have you been?'

Others were coming up and crowding around him now, fitters and riggers and the men who drove the fire tender, and they all waited to hear what Fin would say. He stood there pulling off his helmet, pushing back his black hair with his hand, and he was so astonished at our behaviour that at first he merely looked at us and did not speak. Then he laughed and he said, 'What in the hell's the matter? What's the matter with all of you?'

'Where have you been?' we shouted. 'Where have you been for two days?'

Upon the face of Fin there was a great and enormous astonishment. He looked quickly at his watch.

'Five past twelve,' he said. 'I left at eleven, one hour and five minutes ago. Don't be a lot of damn fools. I must go and report quickly. The Navy will want to know that those destroyers are still in the harbour at Beyrouth.'

He started to walk away; I caught his arm.

'Fin,' I said quietly, 'you've been away since the day before yesterday. What's the matter with you?'

He looked at me and laughed.

'I've seen you organize much better jokes than this one,' he said. 'It isn't so funny. It isn't a bit funny.' And he walked away.

We stood there, the Stag, Paddy and I, the fitters, the riggers and the men who drove the fire-engine, watching Fin as he walked away. We looked at each other, not knowing what to say or to think, understanding nothing, knowing nothing except that Fin had been serious when he spoke and that what he said he had believed to be true. We knew this because we knew Fin, and we knew it because when one has been together as we had been together, then there is never any doubting of anything that anyone says when he is talking about his flying: there can only be a doubting of one's self. These men were doubting themselves, standing there in the sun doubting themselves, and the Stag was standing by the wing of Fin's machine peeling off with his fingers little flakes of paint which had dried up and cracked in the sun.

Someone said, 'Well, I'll be buggered,' and the men turned and started to walk quietly back to their jobs. The next three pilots on readiness came walking slowly towards us from the grey corrugated-iron hangar, walking slowly under the heat of the sun and swinging their helmets in their hands as they came. The Stag, Paddy and I walked over to the pilots' mess to have a drink and lunch.

The mess was a small white wooden building with a veranda. Inside there were two rooms, one a sitting-room with armchairs and magazines and a hole in the wall through which you could buy drinks, and the other a dining-room with one long wooden table. In the sitting-room we found Fin talking to Monkey, our CO. The other pilots were sitting around listening and everybody was drinking beer. We knew that it was really a serious business in spite of the beer and the armchairs; that Monkey was doing what he had to do and doing it in the only way possible. Monkey was a rare man, tall with a handsome face, an Italian bullet wound in his leg and a casual friendly efficiency. He never laughed out loud, he just choked and grunted deep in his throat.

Fin was saying, 'You must go easy, Monkey; you must help me to stop thinking that I've gone mad.'

Fin was being serious and sensible, but he was worried as hell.

'I have told you all I know,' he said. 'That I took off at

eleven o'clock, that I climbed up high, that I flew to Bey-routh, saw the two French destroyers and came back, landing at five past twelve. I swear to you that that is all I know.'

He looked around at us, at the Stag and me, at Paddy and Johnny and the half-dozen other pilots in the room, and we smiled at him and nodded to show him that we were with him, not against him, and that we believed what he said.

Monkey said, 'What in the hell am I going to say to Headquarters at Jerusalem? I reported you missing. Now I've got to report your return. They'll insist on knowing where you've been.'

The whole thing was getting to be too much for Fin. He was sitting upright, tapping with the fingers of his left hand on the leather arm of his chair, tapping with quick sharp taps, leaning forward, thinking, thinking, fighting to think, tapping on the arm of the chair and then he began tapping the floor with his foot as well. The Stag could stand it no longer.

'Monkey,' he said, 'Monkey, let's just leave it all for a bit. Let's leave it and perhaps Fin will remember something later on.'

Paddy, who was sitting on the arm of the Stag's chair, said, 'Yes, and meanwhile we could tell HQ that Fin had force-landed in a field in Syria, taken two days to repair his aircraft, then flown home.'

Everybody was helping Fin. The pilots were all helping him. In the mind of each of us was the certain knowledge that here was something that concerned us greatly. Fin knew it, although that was all he knew, and the others knew it because one could see it upon their faces. There was a tension, a fine high-drawn tension in the room, because here for the first time was something which was neither bullets nor fire nor the coughing of an engine nor burst tyres nor blood in the cockpit nor yesterday nor today, nor even tomorrow. Monkey felt it too, and he said, 'Yes, let's have another drink and leave it for a bit. I'll tell HQ that you force-landed in Syria and managed to get off again later.'

We had some more beer and went in to lunch. Monkey ordered bottles of Palestine white wine with the meal to celebrate Fin's return.

After that no one mentioned the thing at all; we did not even talk about it when Fin wasn't there. But each one of us continued to think about it secretly, knowing for certain that it was something important and that it was not finished. The tension spread quickly through the squadron and it was with all the pilots.

Meanwhile the days went by and the sun shone upon the aerodrome and upon the aircraft and Fin took his place among us flying in the normal way.

Then one day, I think it was about a week later, we did another ground-strafe of Rayak aerodrome. There were six of us, with Monkey leading and Fin flying on his starboard side. We came in low over Rayak and there was plenty of light flak, and as we went in on the first run, Paddy's machine was hit. As we wheeled for the second run we saw his Hurricane wing gently over and dive straight to the ground at the edge of the aerodrome. There was a great billow of white smoke as it hit, then the flames, and as the flames spread the smoke turned from white to black and Paddy was with it. Immediately there was a crackle over the radio and I heard Fin's voice, very excited, shouting into his microphone, shouting, 'I've remembered it. Hello, Monkey, I've remembered it all,' and Monkey's calm slow reply, 'OK, Fin, OK; don't forget it.'

We did our second run and then Monkey led us quickly away, weaving in and out of the valleys, with the bare grey-brown hills far above us on either side, and all the way home, all through the half-hour's flight, Fin never stopped shouting over the RT. First he would call to Monkey and say, 'Hello, Monkey, I've remembered it, all of it; every bit of it.' Then he would say, 'Hello, Stag, I've remembered it, all of it; I can't forget it now.' He called me and he called Johnny and he called Wishful; he called us all separately over and over again, and he was so excited that sometimes he shouted too loudly into his mike and we could not hear what he was saying.

When we landed, we dispersed our aircraft and because Fin for some reason had to park his at the far side of the aerodrome, the rest of us were in the operations room before him.

The ops room was beside the hangar. It was a bare place with a large table in the middle of the floor on which there was a map of the area. There was another smaller table with a couple of telephones, a few wooden chairs and benches and at one end the floor was stacked with Mae Wests, parachutes and helmets. We were standing there taking off our flying clothing and throwing it on to the floor at the end of the room when Fin arrived. He came quickly into the doorway and stopped. His black hair was standing up straight and untidy because of the way in which he had pulled off his helmet; his face was shiny with sweat and his khaki shirt was dark and wet. His mouth was open and he was breathing quickly. He looked as though he had been running. He looked like a child who had rushed downstairs into a room full of grown-ups to say that the cat has had kittens in the nursery and who does not know how to begin.

We had all heard him coming because that was what we had been waiting for. Everyone stopped what they were doing and stood still, looking at Fin.

Monkey said, 'Hello, Fin,' and Fin said, 'Monkey, you've got to believe this because it's what happened.'

Monkey was standing over by the table with the telephones; the Stag was near him, square short ginger-haired Stag, standing up straight, holding a Mae West in his hand, looking at Fin. The others were at the far end of the room. When Fin spoke, they began to move up quietly until they were closer to him, until they reached the edge of the big map table which they touched with their hands. There they stood, looking at Fin, waiting for him to begin.

He started at once, talking quickly, then calming down and talking more slowly as he got into his story. He told everything, standing there by the door of the ops room, with his yellow Mae West still on him and with his helmet and oxygen mask in his hand. The others stayed where they were and listened, and as I listened to him, I forgot that it was Fin speaking and that we were in the ops room at Haifa; I forgot everything and went with him on his journey, and did not come back until he had finished.

'I was flying at about twenty thousand,' he said. 'I flew over Tyre and Sidon and over the Damour River and then I flew inland over the Lebanon hills, because I intended to approach Beyrouth from the east. Suddenly I flew into cloud, thick white cloud which was so thick and dense that I could see nothing except the inside of my cockpit. I couldn't understand it, because a moment before everything had been clear and blue and there had been no cloud anywhere.

'I started to lose height to get out of the cloud and I went down and down and still I was in it. I knew that I must not go too low because of the hills, but at six thousand the cloud was still around me. It was so thick that I could see nothing, not even the nose of my machine nor the wings, and the cloud condensed on the windshield and little rivers of water ran down the glass and got blown away by the slipstream. I have never seen cloud like that before. It was thick and white right up to the edges of the cockpit. I felt like a man on a magic carpet, sitting there alone in this little glass-topped cockpit, with no wings, no tail, no engine and no aeroplane.

'I knew that I must get out of this cloud, so I turned and flew west over the sea away from the mountains; then I came down low by my altimeter. I came down to five hundred feet, four hundred, three hundred, two hundred, one hundred, and the cloud was still around me. For a moment I paused. I knew that it was unsafe to go lower.

Then, quite suddenly, like a gust of wind, came the feeling that there was nothing below me; no sea nor earth nor anything else, and slowly, deliberately, I opened the throttle, pushed the stick hard forward and dived.

'I did not watch the altimeter; I looked straight ahead through the windshield at the whiteness of the cloud and I went on diving. I sat there pressing the stick forward, keeping her in the dive, watching the vast clinging whiteness of the cloud and I never once wondered where I was going. I just went.

'I do not know how long I sat there; it may have been minutes and it may have been hours; I know only that as I sat there and kept her diving, I was certain that what was below me was neither mountains nor rivers nor earth nor sea and I was not afraid.

'Then I was blinded. It was like being half asleep in bed when someone turns on the light.

'I came out of the cloud so suddenly and so quickly that I was blinded. There was no space of time between being in it and being out of it. One moment I was in it and the whiteness was thick around me and in that same moment I was out of it and the light was so bright that I was blinded. I screwed up my eyes and held them tight closed for several seconds.

'When I opened them everything was blue, more blue than anything that I had ever seen. It was not a dark blue, nor was it a bright blue; it was a blue blue, a pure shining colour which I had never seen before and which I cannot describe. I looked around. I looked up above me and behind me. I sat up and peered below me through the glass of the cockpit and everywhere it was blue. It was bright and clear, like pleasant sunlight, but there was no sun.

'Then I saw them.

'Far ahead and above I saw a long thin line of aircraft flying across the sky. They were moving forward in a single black line, all at the same speed, all in the same direction, all close up, following one behind the other, and the line stretched across the sky as far as the eye could see. It was the way they moved ahead, the urgent way in which they pressed forward forward forward like ships sailing before a great wind, it was from this that I knew everything. I do not know why or how I knew it, but I knew as I looked at them that these were the pilots and air crews who had been killed in battle, who now, in their own aircraft were making their last flight, their last journey.

'As I flew higher and closer I could recognize the machines themselves. I saw in that long procession nearly every type there was. I saw Lancasters and Dorniers, Halifaxes and Hurricanes, Messerschmitts, Spitfires, Stirlings, Savoia 79s, Junkers 88s, Gladiators, Hampdens, Macchi 200s, Blenheims, Focke Wulfs, Beaufighters, Swordfish and Heinkels. All these and many more I saw, and the moving line reached across the blue sky both to the one side and to the other until it faded from sight.

'I was close to them now and I began to sense that I was being sucked towards them regardless of what I wished to do. There was a wind which took hold of my machine, blew it over and tossed it about like a leaf and I was pulled and sucked as by a giant vortex towards the other aeroplanes. There was nothing I could do for I was in the vortex and in the arms of the wind. This all happened very quickly, but I remember it clearly. I felt the pull on my aircraft becoming stronger; I was whisked forward faster and faster, and then suddenly I was flying in the procession itself, moving forward with the others, at the same speed and on the same course. Ahead of me, close enough for me to see the colour of the paint on its wings, was a Swordfish, an old Fleet Air Arm Swordfish. I could see the heads and helmets of the observer and the pilot as they sat in their cockpits, the one behind the other. Ahead of the Swordfish there was a Dornier, a Flying Pencil, and beyond the Dornier there were others which I could not recognize from where I was.

'We flew on and on. I could not have turned and flown away even if I had wanted to. I do not know why, although it may have been something to do with the vortex and with the wind, but I knew that it was so. Moreover, I was not really flying my aircraft; it flew itself. There was no manoeuvring to reckon with, no speed, no height, no throttle, no stick, no nothing. Once I glanced down at my instruments and saw that they were all dead, just as they are when the machine is sitting on the ground.

'So we flew on. I had no idea how fast we went. There was no sensation of speed and for all I know, it was a million miles an hour. Now I come to think of it, I never once during that time felt either hot or cold or hungry or thirsty; I felt none of those things. I felt no fear, because I knew nothing of which to be afraid. I felt no worry, because I could remember nothing or think of nothing about which to be worried. I felt no desire to do anything that I was not doing or to have anything that I did not have, because there was nothing that I wished to do and there was nothing that I wished to have. I felt only pleasure at being where I was, at seeing the wonderful light and the beautiful colour around me. Once I caught sight of my face in the cockpit mirror and I saw that I was smiling, smiling with my eyes and with my mouth, and when I looked away I knew that I was still smiling, simply because that was the way I felt. Once, the observer in the Swordfish ahead of me turned and waved his hand. I slid back the roof of my cockpit and waved back. I remember that even when I opened the cockpit, there was no rush of air and no rush of cold or heat, nor was there any pressure of the slipstream on my hand. Then I noticed that they were all waving at each other, like children on a rollercoaster, and I turned and waved at the man in the Macchi behind me.

'But there was something happening along the line. Far up in front I could see that the aeroplanes had changed course, were wheeling around to the left and losing height. The whole procession, as it reached a certain point, was banking around and gliding downwards in a wide, sweeping circle. Instinctively I glanced down over the cockpit, and there I saw spread out below me a vast green plain. It was green and smooth and beautiful; it reached to the far edges of the horizon where the blue of the sky came down and merged with the green of the plain.

'And there was the light. Over to the left, far away in the distance, was a bright white light, shining bright and without any colour. It was as though the sun, but something far bigger than the sun, something without shape or form whose light was bright but not blinding, was lying on the far edge of the green plain. The light spread outwards from a centre of brilliance and it spread far up into the sky and far out over the plain. When I saw it, I could not at first look away from it. I had a desire to go towards it, into it, and almost at once the desire and the longing became so intense that several times I tried to pull my aircraft out of the line and fly straight towards it; but it was not possible and I had to fly with the rest.

'As they banked around and lost height I went with them, and we began to glide down towards the green plain below. Now that I was closer, I could see the great mass of aircraft upon the plain itself. They were everywhere, scattered over the ground like currants upon a green carpet. There were hundreds and hundreds of them, and each minute, each second almost, their number grew as those in front of me landed and taxied to a standstill.

'Quickly we lost height. Soon I saw that the ones just in front of me were lowering their wheels and preparing to land. The Dornier next but one to me levelled off and touched down. Then the old Swordfish. The pilot turned a little to the left out of the way of the Dornier and landed beside him. I turned to the left of the Swordfish and levelled off. I looked out of the cockpit at the ground, judging the height, and I saw the green of the ground blurred as it rushed past me and below me.

'I waited for my aircraft to sink and to touch down. It seemed to take a long time. "Come on," I said. "Come on, come on." I was only about six feet up, but she would not sink. "Get down," I shouted, "please *get down*." I began to panic. I became frightened. Suddenly I noticed that I was gaining speed. I cut all the switches but it made no difference. The aircraft was gathering speed, going faster and faster, and I looked around and saw behind me the long procession of aircraft dropping down out of the sky and sweeping in to land. I saw the mass of machines upon the ground, scattered far across the plain, and away on one side I saw the light, that shining white light which shone so brightly over the great plain and to which I longed to go. I know that had I been able to land, I would have started to run towards that light the moment I got out of my aircraft.

'And now I was flying away from it. My fear grew. As I flew faster and farther away, the fear took hold of me until soon I was fighting crazy mad, pulling at the stick, wrestling with the aeroplane, trying to turn it around, back towards the light. When I saw that it was impossible, I tried to kill myself. I really wanted to kill myself then. I tried to dive the aircraft into the ground, but it flew on straight. I tried to jump out of the cockpit, but there was a hand upon my shoulder which held me down. I tried to bang my head against the sides of the cockpit, but it made no difference and I sat there fighting with my machine and with everything until suddenly I noticed that I was in cloud. I was in the same thick white cloud as before; and I seemed to be climbing. I looked behind me, but the cloud had closed in all round. There was nothing now but this vast impenetrable whiteness. I began to feel sick and giddy. I did not care any longer what happened one way or the other, I just sat there limply, letting the machine fly on by itself.

'It seemed a long time and I am sure that I sat there for many hours. I must have gone to sleep. As I slept, I dreamed. I dreamed not of the things that I had just seen, but of the things of my ordinary life, of the squadron, of Nikki and of the aerodrome here at Haifa. I dreamed that I was sitting at readiness outside the hangar with two others, that a request came from the Navy for someone to do a quick recco over Beyrouth; and because I was first up, I jumped into my Hurricane and went off. I dreamed that I passed over Tyre and Sidon and over the Damour River, climbing up to twenty thousand as I went. Then I turned inland over the Lebanon hills, swung around and approached Beyrouth from the east. I was above the town, peering over the side of the cockpit, looking for the harbour and trying to find the two French destroyers. Soon I saw them, saw them clearly, tied up close alongside each other by the wharf, and I banked around and dived for home as fast as I could.

'The Navy's wrong, I thought to myself as I flew back. The destroyers are still in the harbour. I looked at my watch. An hour and a half. "I've been quick," I said. "They'll be pleased." I tried to call up on the radio to give the information, but I couldn't get through.

'Then I came back here. When I landed, you all crowded around me and asked me where I had been for two days, but I could remember nothing. I did not remember anything except the flight to Beyrouth until just now, when I saw Paddy being shot down. As his machine hit the ground, I found myself saying, "You lucky bastard. You lucky, lucky bastard," and as I said it, I knew why I was saying it and remembered everything. That was when I shouted to you over the radio. That was when I remembered.'

Fin had finished. No one had moved or said anything all the time that he had been talking. Now it was only Monkey who spoke. He shuffled his feet on the floor, turned and looked out of the window and said quietly, almost in a whisper, 'Well, I'll be damned,' and the rest of us went slowly back to the business of taking off our flying clothing and stacking it in the corner of the room on the floor; all except the Stag, square short Stag, who stood there watching Fin as Fin walked slowly across the room to put away his clothing.

After Fin's story, the squadron returned to normal. The tension which had been with us for over a week disappeared. The aerodrome was a happier place in which to be. But no one ever mentioned Fin's journey. We never once spoke about it together, not even when we got drunk in the evening at the Excelsior in Haifa.

The Syrian campaign was coming to an end. Everyone could see that it must finish soon, although the Vichy people were still fighting fiercely south of Beyrouth. We were still flying. We were flying a great deal over the fleet, which was bombarding the coast, for we had the job of protecting them from the Junkers 88s which came over from Rhodes. It was on the last one of these flights over the fleet that Fin was killed.

We were flying high above the ships when the Ju 88s came over in force and there was a battle. We had only six Hurricanes in the air; there were many of the Junkers and it was a good fight. I do not remember much about what went on at the time. One never does. But I remember that it was a hectic, chasing fight, with the Junkers diving for the ships, with the ships barking at them, throwing up everything into the air so that the sky was full of white flowers which blossomed quickly and grew and blew away with the wind. I remember the German who blew up in mid-air, quickly, with just a white flash, so that where the bomber had been, there was nothing left except tiny little pieces falling slowly downwards. I remember the one that had its rear turret shot away, which flew along with the gunner hanging out of the tail by his straps, struggling to get back into the machine. I remember one, a brave one who stayed up above to fight us while the others went down to dive-bomb. I remember that we shot him up and I remember seeing him turn slowly over on to his back, pale-green belly upwards like a dead fish, before finally he spun down.

And I remember Fin.

I was close to him when his aircraft caught fire. I could see the flames coming out of the nose of his machine and dancing over the engine cowling. There was black smoke coming from the exhaust of his Hurricane.

I flew up close and I called to him over the RT. 'Hello, Fin,' I called, 'you'd better jump.'

His voice came back, calm and slow. 'It's not so easy.'

'Jump,' I shouted. 'Jump quickly.'

I could see him sitting there under the glass roof of the cockpit. He looked towards me and shook his head.

'It's not so easy,' he answered. 'I'm a bit shot up. My arms are shot up and I can't undo the straps.'

'Get out,' I shouted. 'For God's sake, get out,' but he did not answer. For a moment his aircraft flew on, straight and level, then gently, like a dying eagle, it dipped a wing and dived towards the sea. I watched it as it went; I watched the thin trail of black smoke which it made across the sky, and as I watched, Fin's voice came again over the radio, clear and slow. 'I'm a lucky bastard,' he was saying. 'A lucky, lucky bastard.'

Death of an Old Man

First published in *Ladies' Home Journal*
(September 1945)

Oh God, how I am frightened.

Now that I am alone I don't have to hide it; I don't have
to hide anything any longer. I can let my face go because
no one can see me; because there's twenty-one thousand
feet between me and them and because now that it's
happening again I couldn't pretend any more even if I
wanted to. Now I don't have to press my teeth together
and tighten the muscles of my jaw as I did during lunch
when the corporal brought in the message; when he
handed it to Tinker and Tinker looked up at me and said,
'Charlie, it's your turn. You're next up.' As if I didn't know
that. As if I didn't know that I was next up. As if I didn't
know it last night when I went to bed, and at midnight
when I was still awake and all the way through the night,
at one in the morning and at two and three and four and
five and six and at seven o'clock when I got up. As if I
didn't know it while I was dressing and while I was having
breakfast and while I was reading the magazines in the
mess, playing shove-halfpenny in the mess, reading the
notices in the mess, playing billiards in the mess. I knew
it then and I knew it when we went in to lunch, while we
were eating that mutton for lunch. And when the corporal came into the room with the message – it wasn't

anything at all. It wasn't anything more than when it begins to rain because there is a black cloud in the sky. When he handed the paper to Tinker I knew what Tinker was going to say before he had opened his mouth. I knew exactly what he was going to say.

So that wasn't anything either.

But when he folded the message up and put it in his pocket and said, 'Finish your pudding. You've got plenty of time,' that was when it got worse, because I knew for certain then that it was going to happen again, that within half an hour I would be strapping myself in and testing the engine and signalling to the airmen to pull away the chocks. The others were all sitting around eating their pudding; mine was still on my plate in front of me, and I couldn't take another mouthful. But it was fine when I tightened my jaw muscles and said, 'Thank God for that. I'm tired of sitting around here picking my nose.' It was certainly fine when I said that. It must have sounded like any of the others just before they started off. And when I got up to leave the table and said, 'See you at teatime,' that must have sounded all right too.

But now I don't have to do any of that. Thank Christ I don't have to do that now. I can just loosen up and let myself go. I can do or say anything I want so long as I fly this aeroplane properly. It didn't use to be like this. Four years ago it was wonderful. I loved doing it because it was exciting, because the waiting on the aerodrome was nothing more than the waiting before a football game or before going in to bat; and three years ago it was all right too. But then always the three months of resting and the going back again and the resting and the going back; always going back and always getting away with it, everyone saying what a fine pilot, no one knowing what a near thing it was that time near Brussels and how lucky it was that time over Dieppe and how bad it was that other time over Dieppe and how lucky and bad and scared I've been every minute of every trip every week this year. No one knows that. They all say, 'Charlie's a great pilot,' 'Charlie's a born flyer,' 'Charlie's terrific.'

I think he was once, but not any longer.

Each time now it gets worse. At first it begins to grow upon you slowly, coming upon you slowly, creeping up on you from behind, making no noise, so that you do not turn round and see it coming. If you saw it coming, perhaps you could stop it, but there is no warning. It creeps closer and closer, like a cat creeps closer stalking a sparrow, and then when it is right behind you, it doesn't spring like the cat would spring; it just leans forward and whispers in your ear. It touches you gently on the shoulder and whispers to you that you are young, that you have a million things to do and a million things to say, that if you are not careful you will buy it, that you are almost certain to buy it sooner or later, and that when you do you will not be anything any longer; you will just be a charred corpse. It whispers to you about how your corpse will look when it is charred, how black it will be and how it will be twisted and brittle, with the face black and the fingers black and the shoes off the feet because the shoes always come off the feet when you die like that. At first it whispers to you only at night, when you are lying awake in bed at night.

Then it whispers to you at odd moments during the day, when you are doing your teeth or drinking a beer or when you are walking down the passage; and in the end it becomes so that you hear it all day and all night all the time.

There's Ijmuiden. Just the same as ever, with the little knob sticking out just beside it. There are the Frisians, Texel, Vlieland, Terschelling, Ameland, Juist and Norderney. I know them all. They look like bacteria under a microscope. There's the Zuider Zee, there's Holland, there's the North Sea, there's Belgium, and there's the world; there's the whole bloody world right there, with all the people who aren't going to get killed and all the houses and the towns and the sea with all the fish. The fish aren't going to get killed either. I'm the only one that's going to get killed. I don't want to die. Oh God, I don't want to die. I don't want to die today anyway. And it isn't the pain. Really it isn't the pain. I don't mind having my leg mashed or my arm burned off; I swear to you that I don't mind that. But I don't want to die. Four years ago I didn't mind. I remember distinctly not minding about it four years ago. I didn't mind about it three years ago either. It was all fine and exciting; it always is when it looks as though you may be going to lose, as it did then. It is always fine to fight when you are going to lose everything anyway, and that was how it was four years ago. But now we're going to win. It is so different when you are going to win. If I die now I lose fifty years of life, and I don't want to lose that. I'll lose anything except that because that would be all the things I want to do and all the things I want to see; all the things like going on sleeping with Joey. Like going home sometimes. Like walking through a wood. Like pouring out a drink from a bottle. Like looking forward to weekends and like being alive every hour every day every year for fifty years. If I die now I will miss all that, and I will miss everything else. I will miss the things that I don't know about. I think those are really the things I am frightened of missing. I think the reason I do not want to die is because of the things I hope will happen. Yes, that's right. I'm sure that's right. Point a revolver at a tramp, at a wet shivering tramp on the side of the road, and say, 'I'm going to shoot you,' and he will cry, 'Don't shoot. Please don't shoot.' The tramp clings to life because of the things he hopes will happen. I am clinging to it for the same reason; but I have clung for so long now that I cannot hold on much longer. Soon I will have to let go. It is like hanging over the edge of a cliff, that's what it is like; and I've been hanging on too long now, holding on to the top of the cliff with my fingers, not being able to pull myself back up, with my fingers getting more and more tired, beginning to hurt and to ache, so that I know that sooner or later I will have to let go. I dare not cry out for help; that is one thing that I dare not do; so I go on hanging over the side of this cliff, and as I hang I keep kicking a little with my feet against the side of the cliff, trying desperately to find a foothold, but it is steep and smooth like the side of a ship, and there isn't any foothold. I am kicking now, that's what I am doing. I am kicking against the smooth side of the cliff, and there isn't any foothold. Soon I shall have to let go. The longer I hang on the more certain I am of that, and so each hour, each day, each night, each week, I become more and more frightened. Four years ago I wasn't hanging over the edge like this. I was running about in the field above, and although I knew that there was a cliff somewhere and that I might fall over it, I did not mind. Three years ago it was the same, but now it is different.

I know that I am not a coward. I am certain of that. I will always keep going. Here I am today, at two o'clock in the afternoon, sitting here flying a course of one hundred and thirty-five at three hundred and sixty miles an hour and flying well; and although I am so frightened that I can hardly think, yet I am going on to do this thing. There was never any question of not going or of turning back. I would rather die than turn back. Turning back never enters into it. It would be easier if it did. I would prefer to have to fight that than to have to fight this fear.

There's Wassalt. Little camouflaged group of buildings and great big camouflaged aerodrome, probably full of 109s and 190s. Holland looks wonderful. It must be a lovely place in the summer. I expect they are haymaking down there now. I expect the German soldiers are watching the Dutch girls haymaking. Bastards. Watching them haymaking, then making them come home with them afterwards. I would like to be haymaking now. I would like to be haymaking and drinking cider.

The pilot was sitting upright in the cockpit. His face was nearly hidden by his goggles and by his oxygen mask. His right hand was resting lightly upon the stick, and his left hand was forward on the throttle. All the time he was looking around him into the sky. From force of habit his head never ceased to move from one side to the other, slowly, mechanically, like clockwork, so that each moment almost, he searched every part of the blue sky, above, below and all around. But it was into the light of the sun itself that he looked twice as long as he looked anywhere else; for that is the place where the enemy hides and waits before he jumps upon you. There are only two places in which you can hide yourself when you are up in the sky. One is in cloud and the other is in the light of the sun.

He flew on; and although his mind was working upon many things and although his brain was the brain of a frightened man, yet his instinct was the instinct of a pilot who is in the sky of the enemy. With a quick glance, without stopping the movement of his head, he looked down and checked his instruments. The glance took no more than a second, and like a camera can record a dozen things at once with the opening of a shutter, so he at a glance recorded with his eyes his oil pressure, his petrol, his oxygen, his rev counter, boost and his air-speed, and in the same instant almost he was looking up again into the sky. He looked at the sun, and as he looked, as he screwed up his eyes and searched into the dazzling brightness of the sun, he thought that he saw something. Yes, there it was; a small black speck moving slowly across the bright surface of the sun, and to him the speck was not a speck but a life-size German pilot sitting in a Focke Wulf which had cannon in its wings.

He knew that he had been seen. He was certain that

the one above was watching him, taking his time, sure of being hidden in the brightness of the sun, watching the Spitfire and waiting to pounce. The man in the Spitfire did not take his eye away from the small speck of black. His head was quite still now. He was watching the enemy, and as he watched, his left hand came away from the throttle and began to move delicately around the cockpit. It moved quickly and surely, touching this thing and that, switching on his reflector sight, turning his trigger button from 'safe' over to 'fire' and pressing gently with his thumb upon a lever which increased, ever so slightly, the pitch of the airscrew.

There was no thought in his head now save for the thought of battle. He was no longer frightened or thinking of being frightened. All that was a dream, and as a sleeper who opens his eyes in the morning and forgets his dream, so this man had seen the enemy and had forgotten that he was frightened. It was always the same. It had happened a hundred times before, and now it was happening again. Suddenly, in an instant, he had become cool and precise, and as he prepared himself, as he made ready his cockpit, he watched the German, waiting to see what he would do.

This man was a great pilot. He was great because when the time came, whenever the moment arrived, his coolness was great and his courage was great, and more than anything else his instinct was great, greater by far than his coolness or his courage or his experience. Now he eased open the throttle and pulled the stick gently backwards, trying to gain height, trying to gain a little of the five-thousand-feet advantage which the German had over him. But there was not much time. The Focke Wulf came out of the sun with its nose down and it came fast. The pilot saw it coming and he kept going straight on, pretending that he had not seen it, and all the time he was looking over his shoulder, watching the German, waiting for the moment to turn. If he turned too soon, the German would turn with him, and he would be duck soup. If he turned too late, the German would get him anyway, provided that he could shoot straight, and he would be duck soup then too. So he watched and waited, turning his head and looking over his shoulder, judging his distance; and as the German came within range, as he was about to press his thumb upon the trigger button, the pilot swerved. He yanked the stick hard back and over to the left, he kicked hard with his left foot upon the rudder bar, and like a leaf which is caught up and carried away by a gust of wind, the Spitfire flipped over on to its side and changed direction. The pilot blacked out.

As his sight came back, as the blood drained away from his head and from his eyes, he looked up and saw the German fighter way ahead, turning with him, banking hard, trying to turn tighter and tighter in order to get back on the tail of the Spitfire. The fight was on. Here we go, he said to himself. Here we go again, and he smiled once, quickly, because he was confident and because he had done this so many times before and because each time he had won.

The man was a beautiful pilot. But the German was good too, and when the Spitfire applied a little flap in order to turn in tighter circles, the Focke Wulf appeared to do the same, and they turned together. When the Spitfire throttled back suddenly and got on his tail, the Focke Wulf half rolled and dived out and under and was away, pulling up again in a loop and rolling off the top, so that he came in again from behind. The Spitfire half rolled and dived away, but the Focke Wulf anticipated him, and half rolled and dived with him, behind him on his tail, and here he took a quick shot at the Spitfire, but he missed. For at least fifteen minutes the two small aircraft rolled and dived around each other in the sky. Sometimes they would separate, wheeling around and around in tight turns, watching one another, circling and watching like two boxers circling each other in the ring, waiting for an opening or for the dropping of a guard; then there would be a stall-turn and one would attack the other, and the diving and the rolling and the zooming would start all over again.

All the time the pilot of the Spitfire sat upright in his cockpit, and he flew his aircraft not with his hands but with the tips of his fingers, and the Spitfire was not a Spitfire but a part of his own body; the muscles of his arms and legs were in the wings and in the tail of the machine so that when he banked and turned and dived and climbed he was not moving his hands and his legs, but only the wings and the tail and the body of the aeroplane; for the body of the Spitfire was the body of the pilot, and there was no difference between the one and the other.

So it went on, and all the while, as they fought and as they flew, they lost height, coming down nearer and nearer to the fields of Holland, so that soon they were fighting only three thousand feet above the ground, and one could see the hedges and the small trees and shadows which the small trees made upon the grass.

Once the German tried a long shot, from a thousand yards, and the pilot of the Spitfire saw the tracer streaming past in front of the nose of his machine. Once, when they flew close past each other, he saw, for a moment, the head and shoulders of the German under the glass roof of his cockpit, the head turned towards him, with the brown helmet, the goggles, the nose and the white scarf. Once when he blacked out from a quick pull-out, the black-out lasted longer than usual. It lasted maybe five seconds, and when his sight came back, he looked quickly around for the Focke Wulf and saw it half a mile away, flying straight at him on the beam, a thin inch-long black line which grew quickly, so that almost at once it was no longer an inch, but an inch and a half, then two inches, then six and then a foot. There was hardly any time. There was a second or perhaps two at the most, but it was enough because he did not have to think or to wonder what to do; he had only to allow his instinct to control his arms and his legs and the wings and the body of the aeroplane. There was only one thing to do, and the Spitfire did it. It banked steeply and turned at right angles towards the Focke Wulf, facing it and flying straight towards it for a head-on attack.

The two machines flew fast towards each other. The pilot of the Spitfire sat upright in his cockpit, and now, more than ever, the aircraft was a part of his body. His eye was upon the reflector sight, the small yellow electric-light dot which was projected up in front of the windshield, and it was upon the thinness of the Focke Wulf beyond. Quickly, precisely, he moved his aircraft a little this way and that, and the yellow dot, which moved with the aircraft, danced and jerked this way and that, and then suddenly it was upon the thin line of the Focke Wulf and there it stayed. His right thumb in the leather glove felt for the firing-button; he squeezed it gently, as a rifleman squeezes a trigger, his guns fired, and at the same time, he saw the small spurts of flame from the cannon in the nose of the Focke Wulf. The whole thing, from beginning to end, took perhaps as long as it would take you to light a cigarette. The German pilot came straight on at him and he had a sudden, vivid, colourless view of the round nose and the thin outstretched wings of the Focke Wulf. Then there was a crack as their wing-tips met, and there was a splintering as the port wing of the Spitfire came away from the body of the machine.

The Spitfire was dead. It fell like a dead bird falls, fluttering a little as it died; continuing in the direction of its flight as it fell. The hands of the pilot, almost in a single movement, undid his straps, tore off his helmet and slid back the hood of the cockpit; then they grasped the edges of the cockpit and he was out and away, falling, reaching for the ripcord, grasping it with his right hand, pulling on it so that his parachute billowed out and opened and the straps jerked him hard between the fork of his legs.

All of a sudden the silence was great. The wind was blowing on his face and in his hair and he reached up a hand and brushed the hair away from his eyes. He was about a thousand feet up, and he looked down and saw flat green country with fields and hedges and no trees. He could see some cows in the field below him. Then he looked up, and as he looked, he said, 'Good God,' and his right hand moved quickly to his right hip, feeling for his revolver, which he had not brought with him. For there, not more than five hundred yards away, parachuting down at the same time and at the same height, was another man, and he knew when he saw him that it could be only the German pilot. Obviously his plane had been damaged at the same time as the Spitfire in the collision. He must have got out quickly too; and now here they were, both of them parachuting down so close to each other that they might even land in the same field.

He looked again at the German, hanging there in his straps with his legs apart, his hands above his head grasping the cords of the parachute. He seemed to be a small man, thickly built and by no means young. The German was looking at him too. He kept looking, and when his body swung around the other way, he turned his head, looking over his shoulder.

So they went on down. Both men were watching each other, thinking about what would happen soon, and the German was the king because he was landing in his own territory. The pilot of the Spitfire was coming down in enemy country; he would be taken prisoner, or he would be killed, or he would kill the German, and if he did that, he would escape. I will escape anyway, he thought. I'm sure I can run faster than the German. He does not look as though he could run very fast. I will race him across the fields and get away.

The ground was close now. There were not many seconds to go. He saw that the German would almost certainly land in the same field as he, the field with the cows. He looked down to see what the field was like and whether the hedges were thick and whether there was a gate in the hedge, and as he looked, he saw below him in the field a small pond, and there was a small stream running through the pond. It was a cow-drinking pond, muddy round the edges and muddy in the water. The pond was right below him. He was no more than the height of a horse above it and he was dropping fast; he was dropping right into the middle of the pond. Quickly he grasped the cords above his head and tried to spill the parachute to one side so that he would change direction, but he was too late; it wasn't any good. All at once something brushed the surface of his brain and the top of his stomach, and the fear which he had forgotten in the fighting was upon him again. He saw the pond and the black surface of the water of the pond, and the pond was not a pond, and the water was not water; it was a small black hole in the surface of the earth which went on down and down for miles and miles, with steep smooth sides like the sides of a ship, and it was so deep that when you fell into it, you went on falling and falling and you fell for ever. He saw the mouth of the hole and the deepness of it, and he was only a small brown pebble which someone had picked up and thrown into the air so that it would fall into the hole. He was a pebble which someone had picked up in the grass of the field. That was all he was and now he was falling and the hole was below him.

Splash. He hit the water. He went through the water and his feet hit the bottom of the pond. They sank into the mud on the bottom and his head went under the water, but it came up again and he was standing with the water up to his shoulders. The parachute was on top of him; his head was tangled in a mass of cords and white silk and he pulled at them with his hands, first this way and then that, but it only got worse, and the fear got worse because the white silk was covering his head so that he could see nothing but a mass of white cloth and a tangle of cords. Then he tried to move towards the bank, but his feet were stuck in the mud; he had sunk up to his knees in the mud. So he fought the parachute and the tangled cords of the parachute, pulling at them with his hands and trying to get them clear of his head; and as he did so he heard the sound of footsteps running on the grass. He heard the noise of the footsteps coming closer and the German must have jumped, because there was a splash and he was knocked over by the weight of a man's body.

He was under the water, and instinctively he began to struggle. But his feet were still stuck in the mud, the man was on top of him and there were hands around his neck holding him under and squeezing his neck with strong fingers. He opened his eyes and saw brown water. He noticed the bubbles in the water, small bright bubbles rising slowly upwards in the brown water. There was no noise or shouting or anything else, but only the bright bubbles moving upwards in the water, and suddenly, as he watched them, his mind became clear and calm like a sunny day. I won't struggle, he thought. There is no point in struggling, for when there is a black cloud in the sky, it is bound to rain.

He relaxed his body and all the muscles in his body because he had no farther wish to struggle. How nice it is not to struggle, he thought. There is no point in struggling. I was a fool to have struggled so much and for so long; I was a fool to have prayed for the sun when there was a black cloud in the sky. I should have prayed for rain; I should have shouted for rain. I should have shouted, Let it rain, let it rain in solid sheets and I will not care. Then it would have been easy. It would have been so easy then. I have struggled for five years and now I don't have to do it any more. This is so much better; this is ever so much better, because there is a wood somewhere that I wish to walk through, and you cannot walk struggling through a wood. There is a girl somewhere that I wish to sleep with, and you cannot sleep struggling with a girl. You cannot do anything struggling; especially you cannot live struggling, and so now I am going to do all the things that I want to do, and there will be no more struggling.

See how calm and lovely it is like this. See how sunny it is and what a beautiful field this is, with the cows and the little pond and the green hedges with primroses growing in the hedges. Nothing will worry me any more now, nothing nothing nothing; not even that man splashing in the water of the pond over there. He seems very puffed and out of breath. He seems to be dragging something out of the pond, something heavy. Now he's got it to the side and he's pulling it up on to the grass. How funny; it's a body. It's a body of a man. As a matter of fact, I think it's me. Yes, it is me. I know it is because of that smudge of yellow paint on the front of my flying suit. Now he's kneeling down, searching in my pockets, taking out my money and my identification card. He's found my pipe and the letter I got this morning from my mother. He's taking off my watch. Now he's getting up. He's going away. He's going to leave my body behind, lying on the grass beside the pond. He's walking quickly away across the field towards the gate. How wet and excited he looks. He ought to relax a bit. He ought to relax like me. He can't be enjoying himself that way. I think I will tell him.

'Why don't you relax a bit?'

Goodness, how he jumped when I spoke to him. And his face; just look at his face. I've never seen a man look as frightened as that. He's starting to run. He keeps looking back over his shoulder, but he keeps on running. But just look at his face; just look how unhappy and frightened he is. I do not want to go with him. I think I'll leave him. I think I'll stay here for a bit. I think I'll go along the hedges and find some primroses, and if I am lucky I may find some white violets. Then I will go to sleep. I will go to sleep in the sun.

Someone Like You

First published in *Town & Country*
(November 1945)

'Beer?'

'Yes, beer.'

I gave the order and the waiter brought the bottles and two glasses. We poured out our own, tipping the glasses and holding the tops of the bottles close to the glass.

'Cheers,' I said.

He nodded. We lifted our glasses and drank.

It was five years since I had seen him, and during that time he had been fighting the war. He had been fighting it right from the beginning up to now and I saw at once how he had changed. From being a young, bouncing boy, he had become someone old and wise and gentle. He had become gentle like a wounded child. He had become old like a tired man of seventy years. He had become so different and he had changed so much that at first it was embarrassing for both of us and it was not easy to know what to say.

He had been flying in France in the early days and he was in Britain during the Battle. He was in the Western Desert when we had nothing and he was in Greece and Crete. He was in Syria and he was at Habbaniya during the rebellion. He was at Alamein. He had been flying in

Sicily and in Italy and then he had gone back and flown again from England. Now he was an old man.

He was small, not more than five feet six, and he had a pale, wide-open face which did not hide anything, and a sharp pointed chin. His eyes were bright and dark. They were never still unless they were looking into your own. His hair was black and untidy. There was a wisp of it always hanging down over his forehead; he kept pushing it back with his hand.

For a while we were awkward and did not speak. He was sitting opposite me at the table, leaning forward a little, drawing lines on the dew of the cold beer glass with his finger. He was looking at the glass, pretending to concentrate upon what he was doing, and to me it seemed as though he had something to say, but that he did not know how to say it. I sat there and picked nuts out of the plate and munched them noisily, pretending that I did not care about anything, not even about making a noise while eating.

Then without stopping his drawing on the glass and without looking up, he said quietly and very slowly, 'Oh God, I wish I was a waiter or a whore or something.'

He picked up his glass and drank the beer slowly and all at once, in two swallows. I knew now that there was something on his mind and I knew that he was gathering courage so that he could speak.

'Let's have another,' I said.

'Yes, let's have a whisky.'

'All right, whisky.'

I ordered two double Scotches and some soda, and we

poured the soda into the Scotch and drank. He picked up his glass and drank, put it down, picked it up again and drank some more. As he put down the glass the second time, he leaned forward and quite suddenly he began to talk.

'You know,' he said, 'you know I keep thinking during a raid, when we are running over the target, just as we are going to release our bombs, I keep thinking to myself, Shall I just jink a little; shall I swerve a fraction to one side, then my bombs will fall on someone else. I keep thinking, Whom shall I make them fall on; whom shall I kill tonight? Which ten, twenty or a hundred people shall I kill tonight? It is all up to me. And now I think about this every time I go out.'

He had taken a small nut and was splitting it into pieces with his thumb-nail as he spoke, looking down at what he was doing because he was embarrassed by his own talk.

He was speaking very slowly. 'It would just be a gentle pressure with the ball of my foot upon the rudder bar; a pressure so slight that I would hardly know that I was doing it, and it would throw the bombs on to a different house and on to other people. It is all up to me, the whole thing is up to me, and each time that I go out I have to decide which ones shall be killed. I can do it with the gentle pressure of the ball of my foot upon the rudder bar. I can do it so that I don't even notice that it is being done. I just lean a little to one side because I am shifting my sitting position. That is all I am doing, and then I kill a different lot of people.'

Now there was no dew left upon the face of the glass,

but he was still running the fingers of his right hand up and down the smooth surface.

'Yes,' he said, 'it is a complicated thought. It is very far-reaching; and when I am bombing I cannot get it out of my mind. You see it is such a gentle pressure with the ball of the foot; just a touch on the rudder bar and the bomb-aimer wouldn't even notice. Each time I go out, I say to myself, Shall it be these or shall it be those? Which ones are the worst? Perhaps if I make a little skid to the left I will get a houseful of lousy women-shooting German soldiers, or perhaps if I make that little skid I will miss getting the soldiers and get an old man in a shelter. How can I know? How can anyone know these things?'

He paused and pushed his empty glass away from him into the middle of the table.

'And so I never jink,' he added, 'at least hardly ever.'

'I jinked once,' I said, 'ground-strafing. I thought I'd kill the ones on the other side of the road instead.'

'Everybody jinks,' he said. 'Shall we have another drink?'

'Yes, let's have another.'

I called the waiter and gave the order, and while we were waiting, we sat looking around the room at the other people. The place was starting to fill up because it was about six o'clock and we sat there looking at the people who were coming in. They were standing around looking for tables, sitting down, laughing and ordering drinks.

'Look at that woman,' I said. 'The one just sitting down over there.'

'What about her?'

'Wonderful figure,' I said. 'Wonderful bosom. Look at her bosom.'

The waiter brought the drinks.

'Did I ever tell you about Stinker?' he said.

'Stinker who?'

'Stinker Sullivan in Malta.'

'No.'

'About Stinker's dog?'

'No.'

'Stinker had a dog, a great big Alsatian, and he loved that dog as though it was his father and his mother and everything else he had, and the dog loved Stinker. It used to follow him around everywhere he went, and when he went on ops it used to sit on the tarmac outside the hangars waiting for him to come back. It was called Smith. Stinker really loved that dog. He loved it like his mother and he used to talk to it all day long.'

'Lousy whisky,' I said.

'Yes, let's have another.'

We got some more whisky.

'Well, anyway,' he went on, 'one day the squadron got orders to fly to Egypt. We had to go at once; not in two hours or later in the day, but at once. And Stinker couldn't find his dog. Couldn't find Smith anywhere. Started running all over the aerodrome yelling for Smith and going mad yelling at everyone asking where he was and yelling, "Smith Smith," all over the aerodrome. Smith wasn't anywhere.'

'Where was he?' I said.

'He wasn't there and we had to go. Stinker had to go

without Smith and he was mad as a hatter. His crew said he kept calling up over the radio asking if they'd found him. All the way to Heliopolis he kept calling up Malta saying, Have you got Smith, and Malta kept saying, No, they hadn't.'

'This whisky is really terrible,' I said.

'Yes. We must have some more.'

We had a waiter who was very quick.

'I was telling you about Stinker,' he said.

'Yes, tell me about Stinker.'

'Well, when we got to Egypt he wouldn't talk about anything except Smith. He used to walk around acting as though the dog was always with him. Damn fool walked around saying, "Come on, Smith, old boy, come on," and he kept looking down and talking to him as he walked along. Kept reaching down and patting the air and stroking this bloody dog that wasn't there.'

'Where was it?'

'Malta, I suppose. Must have been in Malta.'

'Isn't this awful whisky?'

'Terrible. We must have some more when we've finished this.'

'Cheers.'

'Cheers.'

'Waiter. Oh waiter. Yes; again.'

'So Smith was in Malta.'

'Yes,' he said. 'And this damn fool Stinker Sullivan went on like this right up to the time he was killed.'

'Must have been mad.'

'He was. Mad as a hatter. You know once he walked into the Sporting Club at Alexandria at drinking time.'

'That wasn't so mad.'

'He walked into the big lounge and as he went in he held the door open and started calling his dog. Then when he thought the dog had come in, he closed the door and started walking right down the length of the room, stopping every now and then and looking round and saying, "Come on, Smith, old boy, come on." He kept flipping his fingers. Once he got down under a table where two men and two women were drinking. He got on to his hands and knees and said, "Smith, come on out of there; come here at once," and he put out his hand and started dragging nothing at all from under the table. Then he apologized to the people at the table. "This is the hell of a dog," he said to them. You should have seen their faces. He went on like that all down the room and when he came to the other end he held the door open for the dog to go out and then went out after it.'

'Man was mad.'

'Mad as a hatter. And you should have seen their faces. It was full of people drinking and they didn't know whether it was them who were crazy or whether it was Stinker. They kept looking up at each other to make sure that they weren't the only ones who couldn't see the dog. One man dropped his drink.'

'That was awful.'

'Terrible.'

The waiter came and went. The room was full of people now, all sitting at little tables, talking and drinking and wearing their uniforms. The pilot poked the ice down into his glass with his finger.

'He used to jink too,' he said.

'Who?'

'Stinker. He used to talk about it.'

'Jinking isn't anything,' I said. 'It's like not touching the cracks on the pavement when you're walking along.'

'Balls. That's just personal. Doesn't affect anyone else.'

'Well, it's like car-waiting.'

'What's car-waiting?'

'I always do it,' I said.

'What is it?'

'Just as you're going to drive off, you sit back and count twenty, then you drive off.'

'You're mad too,' he said. 'You're like Stinker.'

'It's a wonderful way to avoid accidents. I've never had one in a car yet; at least, not a bad one.'

'You're drunk.'

'No, I always do it.'

'Why?'

'Because then if someone was going to have stepped off the kerb in front of your car, you won't hit them because you started later. You were delayed because you counted twenty, and the person who stepped off the kerb whom you would have hit – you missed him.'

'Why?'

'He stepped off the kerb long before you got there because you counted twenty.'

'That's a good idea.'

'I know it's a good idea.'

'It's a bloody marvellous idea.'

'I've saved lots of lives. And you can drive straight

across intersections because the car you would have hit has already gone by. It went by just a little earlier because you delayed yourself by counting twenty.'

'Marvellous.'

'Isn't it?'

'But it's like jinking,' he said. 'You never really know what would have happened.'

'I always do it,' I said.

We kept right on drinking.

'Look at that woman,' I said.

'The one with the bosom?'

'Yes, marvellous bosom.'

He said slowly, 'I bet I've killed lots of women more beautiful than that one.'

'Not lots with bosoms like that.'

'I'll bet I have. Shall we have another drink?'

'Yes, one for the road.'

'There aren't any other women with bosoms like that,' I said. 'Not in Germany anyway.'

'Oh yes there are. I've killed lots of them.'

'All right. You've killed lots of women with wonderful bosoms.'

He leaned back and waved his hand around the room. 'See all the people in this room?' he said.

'Yes.'

'Wouldn't there be a bloody row if they were all suddenly dead; if they all suddenly fell off their chairs on to the floor dead?'

'What about it?'

'Wouldn't there be a bloody row?'

'Certainly there'd be a row.'

'If all the waiters got together and put stuff in all the drinks and everyone died.'

'There'd be a godalmighty row.'

'Well, I've done that hundreds of times. I've killed more people than there are in this room hundreds of times. So have you.'

'Lots more,' I said. 'But that's different.'

'Same sort of people. Men and women and waiters. All drinking in a pub.'

'That's different.'

'Like hell it is. Wouldn't there be a bloody row if it happened here?'

'Bloody awful row.'

'But we've done it. Lots of times.'

'Hundreds of times,' I said. 'This is nothing.'

'This is a lousy place.'

'Yes, it's lousy. Let's go somewhere else.'

'Finish our drinks.'

We finished our drinks and we both tried to pay the bill, so we tossed for it and I won. It came to sixteen dollars and twenty-five cents. He gave the waiter a two-dollar tip.

We got up and walked around the tables and over to the door.

'Taxi,' he said.

'Yes, must have a taxi.'

There wasn't a doorman. We stood out on the kerb waiting for a taxi to come along and he said, 'This is a good town.'

'Wonderful town,' I said. I felt fine. It was dark outside, but there were a few street-lamps, and we could see the cars going by and the people walking on the other side of the street. There was a thin, quiet drizzle falling, and the wetness on the black street shone yellow under the lights of the cars and under the street-lamps. The tyres of the cars hissed on the wet surface.

'Let's go to a place which has lots of whisky,' he said. 'Lots of whisky and a man with egg on his beard serving it.'

'Fine.'

'Somewhere where there are no other people but just us and the man with egg on his beard. Either that.'

'Yes,' I said. 'Either that or what?'

'Or a place with a hundred thousand people in it.'

'Yes,' I said. 'OK.'

We stood there waiting and we could see the lights of the cars as they came round the bend over to the left, coming towards us with the tyres swishing on the wet surface and going past us up the road to the bridge which goes over the river. We could see the drizzle falling through the beams of their headlights and we stood there waiting for a taxi.

The Soldier

First published in *Someone Like You* (1953)

It was one of those nights that made him feel he knew what it was like to be a blind man: not the shadow of an image for his eyes to discern, not even the forms of the trees visible against the sky.

Out of the darkness he became aware of small rustling noises in the hedge, the breathing of a horse some distance away in the field, the soft thud of a hoof as it moved its foot; and once he heard the rush of a bird flying past him low overhead.

'Jock,' he said, speaking loud. 'We'll go home now.' And he turned and began to walk back up the slope of the lane, the dog pulling ahead, showing the way in the dark.

It must be nearly midnight, he thought. That meant that soon it would be tomorrow. Tomorrow was worse than today. Tomorrow was the worst of all because it was going to become today – and today was now.

Today had not been very nice, especially that business with the splinter.

Stop it, he told himself. There isn't any sense thinking about it. It doesn't do anyone any good thinking about things like that. Think about something else for a change. You can kick out a dangerous thought, you know, if you put another in its place. Go right back as far as you can go.

Let's have some memories of sweet days. The seaside holidays in the summer, wet sand and red buckets and shrimping nets and the slippery seaweedy rocks and the small clear pools and sea anemones and snails and mussels and sometimes one grey translucent shrimp hovering deep down in the beautiful green water.

But how *could* that splinter have got into the sole of his foot without him feeling it?

It is not important. Do you remember hunting for cowries along the margin of the tide, each one so fine and perfect it became a precious jewel to be held in the hand all the way home; and the little orange-coloured scallops, the pearly oyster shells, the tiny bits of emerald glass, a live hermit crab, a cockle, the spine of a skate, and once, but never to be forgotten, the dry seawashed jawbone of a human being with teeth in it, white and wonderful among the shells and pebbles. Oh Mummy, look what I've found! Look, Mummy, look!

But to go back to the splinter. She had really been rather unpleasant about that.

'What do you mean, you didn't notice?' she had asked, scornful.

'I just didn't notice, that's all.'

'I suppose you're going to tell me if I stick a pin into your foot you won't feel it?'

'I didn't say that.'

And then she had jabbed him suddenly in the ankle with the pin she had been using to take out the splinter, and he hadn't been watching so he didn't know about it till she had cried out in a kind of horror. And when he had looked down, the pin was sticking into the flesh all by itself behind the anklebone, almost half of it buried.

'Take it out,' he had said. 'You can poison someone like that.'

'You mean you can't *feel* it?'

'Take it out, will you?'

'You mean it doesn't hurt?'

'The pain is terrible. Take it out.'

'What's the *matter* with you?'

'I said the pain is terrible. Didn't you hear me?'

Why did they *do* things like that to him?

When I was down beside the sea, a wooden spade they gave to me, to dig the sandy shore. My holes were empty as a cup, and every time the sea came up, till it could come no more.

A year ago the doctor had said, 'Shut your eyes. Now tell me whether I'm pushing this toe up or down.'

'Up,' he had said.

'And now?'

'Down. No, up. I think it's up.'

It was peculiar that a neurosurgeon should want to play with his toes.

'Did I get them all right, doctor?'

'You did very well.'

But that was a year ago. He had felt pretty good a year ago. The sort of things that happened now never used to happen then. Take, for example, just one item – the bathroom tap.

Why was the hot tap in the bathroom on a different side this morning? That was a new one.

It is not of the least importance, you understand, but it would be interesting to know why.

Do you think she could have changed it over, taken a spanner and a pipe-wrench and sneaked in during the night and changed it over?

Do you? Well – if you really want to know – yes. The way she'd been acting lately, she'd be quite capable of doing that.

A strange and difficult woman, that's what she was. Mind you, she used not to be, but there's no doubt at all that right now she was as strange and difficult as they come. Especially at night.

Yes, at night. That was the worst time of all – the night.

Why, when he put out his right hand in bed at night, could his fingers not feel what they were touching? He had knocked over the lamp and she had woken up and then sat up suddenly while he was feeling for it on the floor in the dark.

'What are you doing now?'

'I knocked over the lamp. I'm sorry.'

'Oh Christ,' she had said. 'Yesterday it was the glass of water. What's the *matter* with you?'

Once, the doctor had stroked the back of his hand with a feather, and he hadn't been able to feel that either. But he had felt it when the man scratched him with a pin.

'Shut your eyes. No – you mustn't look. Shut them tight. Now tell me if this is hot or cold.'

'Hot.'

'And this?'

'Cold.'

'And this?'

'Cold. I mean hot. Yes, it's hot, isn't it?'

'That's right,' the doctor had said. 'You did very well.'

But that was a year ago.

Why were the switches on the walls, just lately, always a few inches away from the well-remembered places when he felt for them in the dark?

Don't think about it, he told himself. The only thing is not to think about it.

And while we're on the subject, why did the walls of the living-room take on a slightly different shade of colour each day?

Green and blue-green and blue; and sometimes – sometimes slowly swimming like colours seen through the heat-haze of a brazier.

One by one, neatly, like index cards out of a machine, the little questions dropped.

Whose face appeared for one second at the window during dinner? Whose eyes?

'What are you staring at?'

'Nothing,' he had answered. 'But it would be nice if we could draw the curtains, don't you think?'

'Robert, what were you staring at?'

'Nothing.'

'Why were you staring at the window like that?'

'It would be nice if we could draw the curtains, don't you think?' he had answered.

He was going past the place where he had heard the horse in the field and now he could hear it again: the breathing, the soft hoof thuds, and the crunch of grass-cropping that was like the noise of a man munching celery.

'Hello, old horse,' he said, calling loud into the darkness. 'Hello, old horse over there.'

Suddenly he heard the footsteps behind him, slow, long-striding footsteps close behind, and he stopped. The footsteps stopped. He turned around, searching the darkness.

'Good evening,' he said. 'You here again?'

In the quiet that followed he could hear the wind moving the leaves in the hedge.

'Are you going my way?' he said.

Then he turned and walked on, the dog still pulling ahead, and the footsteps started after him again, but more softly now, as though the person were walking on toes.

He stopped and turned again.

'I can't see you,' he said, 'because it's so dark. Are you someone I know?'

Again the silence, and the cool summer wind on his cheeks, and the dog tugging on the leash to get home.

'All right,' he called. 'You don't have to answer if you don't want to. But remember I know you're there.'

Someone trying to be clever.

Far away in the night, over to the west and very high, he heard the faint hum of an aeroplane. He stopped again, head up, listening.

'Miles away,' he said. 'Won't come near here.'

But why, when one of them flew over the house, did everything inside him come to a stop, and his talking and what he was doing, while he sat or stood in a sort of paralysis waiting for the whistle-shriek of the bomb. That one after dinner this evening.

'Why did you duck like that?' she had asked.

'Duck?'

'Why did you duck? What are you ducking for?'

'Duck?' he had said again. 'I don't know what you mean.'

'I'll say you don't,' she had answered, staring at him hard with those hard, blue-white eyes, the lids dropping slightly, as always when there was contempt. The drop of her eyelids was something beautiful to him, the half-closed eyes and the way the lids dropped and the eyes became hooded when her contempt was extreme.

Yesterday, lying in bed in the early morning, when the noise of gunfire was just beginning far away down the valley, he had reached out with his left hand and touched her body for a little comfort.

'What on earth are you doing?'

'Nothing, dear.'

'You woke me up.'

'I'm sorry.'

It would be a help if she would only let him lie closer to her in the early mornings when he began to hear the noise of gunfire.

He would soon be home now. Around the last bend of the lane he could see a light glowing pink through the curtain of the living-room window, and he hurried forward to the gate and through it and up the path to the front door, the dog still pulling ahead.

He stood on the porch, feeling around for the door-knob in the dark.

It was on the right when he went out. He distinctly remembered it being on the right-hand side when he shut the door half an hour ago and went out.

It couldn't be that she had changed *that* over too? Just to fox him? Taken a bag of tools and quickly changed it over to the other side while he was out walking the dog?

He moved his hand over to the left – and the moment the fingers touched the knob, something small but violent exploded inside his head and with it a surge of fury and outrage and fear. He opened the door, shut it quickly behind him and shouted, 'Edna, are you there?'

There was no answer so he shouted again, and this time she heard him.

'What do you want now? You woke me up.'

'Come down here a moment, will you. I want to talk to you.'

'Oh for heaven's sake,' she answered. 'Be quiet and come on up.'

'Come here!' he shouted. 'Come here at once!'

'I'll be damned if I will. You come here.'

The man paused, head back, looking up the stairs into the dark of the second floor. He could see where the stair-rail curved to the left and went on up out of sight in the black towards the landing and if you went straight on across the landing you came to the bedroom, and it would be black in there too.

'Edna!' he shouted. 'Edna!'

'Oh go to hell.'

He began to move slowly up the stairs, treading quietly, touching the stair-rail for guidance, up and around the left-hand curve into the dark above. At the top he took an extra step that wasn't there; but he was ready for it and there was no noise. He paused awhile then, listening, and he wasn't sure, but he thought he could hear the guns starting up again far away down the valley, heavy stuff mostly, seventy-fives and maybe a couple of mortars somewhere in the background.

Across the landing now and through the open doorway – which was easy in the dark because he knew it so well – through on to the bedroom carpet that was thick and soft and pale grey although he could not feel or see it.

In the centre of the room he waited, listening for sounds. She had gone back to sleep and was breathing rather loud, making the slightest little whistle with the air between her teeth each time she exhaled. The curtain flapped gently against the open window, the alarm-clock tick-tick-ticked beside the bed.

Now that his eyes were becoming accustomed to the dark he could just make out the end of the bed, the white blanket tucked in under the mattress, the bulge of her feet under the bedclothes; and then, as though aware of the presence of the man in the room, the woman stirred. He heard her turn, and turn again. The sound of her breathing stopped. There was a succession of little movement-noises and once the bedsprings creaked, loud as a shout in the dark.

'Is that you, Robert?'

He made no move, no sound.

'Robert, are you there?'

The voice was strange and rather unpleasant to him.

'Robert!' She was wide awake now. 'Where are you?'

Where had he heard that voice before? It had a quality of stridence, dissonance, like two single high notes struck together hard in discord. Also there was an inability to pronounce the R of Robert. Who was it that used to say Wobert to him?

'Wobert,' she said again. 'What are you doing?'

Was it that nurse in the hospital, the tall one with fair hair? No, it was farther back. Such an awful voice as that he ought to remember. Give him a little time and he would get the name.

At that moment he heard the snap of the switch of the bedside lamp and in the flood of light he saw the woman half-sitting up in bed, dressed in some sort of a pink nightdress. There was a surprised, wide-eyed expression on her face. Her cheeks and chin were oily with cold cream.

'You better put that thing down,' she was saying, 'before you cut yourself.'

'Where's Edna?' He was staring at her hard.

The woman, half-sitting up in bed, watched him carefully. He was standing at the foot of the bed, a huge, broad man, standing motionless, erect, with heels together, almost at attention, dressed in his dark-brown, woolly, heavy suit.

'Go on,' she ordered. 'Put it down.'

'Where's Edna?'

'What's the matter with you, Wobert?'

'There's nothing the matter with me. I'm just asking you where's my wife?'

The woman was easing herself up gradually into an erect sitting position and sliding her legs towards the edge of the bed. 'Well,' she said at length, the voice changing, the hard blue-white eyes secret and cunning, 'if you really want to know, Edna's gone. She left just now while you were out.'

'Where did she go?'

'She didn't say.'

'And who are you?'

'I'm just a friend of hers.'

'You don't have to shout at me,' he said. 'What's all the excitement?'

'I simply want you to know I'm not Edna.'

The man considered this a moment, then he said, 'How did you know my name?'

'Edna told me.'

Again he paused, studying her closely, still slightly puzzled, but much calmer now, his eyes calm, perhaps even a little amused the way they looked at her.

'I think I prefer Edna.'

In the silence that followed they neither of them moved. The woman was very tense, sitting up straight with her arms tense on either side of her and slightly bent at the elbows, the hands pressing palms downward on the mattress.

'I love Edna, you know. Did she ever tell you I love her?'

The woman didn't answer.

'I think she's a bitch. But it's a funny thing I love her just the same.'

The woman was not looking at the man's face; she was watching his right hand.

'Awful cruel little bitch, Edna.'

And a long silence now, the man standing erect, motionless, the woman sitting motionless in the bed, and it was so quiet suddenly that through the open window they could hear the water in the millstream going over the dam far down the valley on the next farm.

Then the man again, speaking calmly, slowly, quite impersonally: 'As a matter of fact, I don't think she even likes me any more.'

The woman shifted closer to the edge of the bed. 'Put that knife down,' she said, 'before you cut yourself.'

'Don't shout, please. Can't you talk nicely?' Now, suddenly, the man leaned forward, staring intently into the woman's face, and he raised his eyebrows. 'That's strange,' he said. 'That's very strange.'

He took a step forward, his knees touching the bed.

'You look a bit like Edna yourself.'

'Edna's gone out. I told you that.'

He continued to stare at her and the woman kept quite still, the palms of her hands pressing deep into the mattress.

'Well,' he said. 'I wonder.'

'I told you Edna's gone out. I'm a friend of hers. My name is Mary.'

'My wife,' the man said, 'has a funny little brown mole just behind her left ear. You don't have that, do you?'

'I certainly don't.'

'Turn your head and let me look.'

'I told you I didn't have it.'

'Just the same, I'd like to make sure.'

The man came slowly around the end of the bed. 'Stay where you are,' he said. 'Please don't move.' And he came towards her slowly, watching her all the time, a little smile touching the corners of his mouth.

The woman waited until he was within reach, and then, with a quick right hand, so quick he never even saw it coming, she smacked him hard across the front of the face. And when he sat down on the bed and began to cry, she took the knife from his hand and went swiftly out of the room, down the stairs to the hall, where the telephone was.

We believe in doing good things.

That's why ten per cent of all Roald Dahl income*
goes to our charity partners. We have supported
causes including: specialist children's nurses,
grants for families in need, and educational
outreach programmes. Thank you for helping
us to sustain this vital work.

Find out more at roalddahl.com

ROALD DAHL

Roald Dahl was a spy, ace fighter pilot, chocolate historian and medical inventor. He was also the author of *Charlie and the Chocolate Factory*, *Matilda*, *The BFG* and many more brilliant stories. He remains the World's No.1 storyteller.

CHARMING BAKER

Born in Hampshire in 1964, Charming Baker spent much of his early life travelling around the world following his father, a commando in the British Army. At the age of twelve, he and his family finally settled in Ripon, North Yorkshire. Baker left school at sixteen and worked in various manual jobs. In 1985, having gone back to college, he was accepted on to a course at the prestigious Central Saint Martins, where he later returned as a lecturer. After graduating, Baker worked for many years as a commercial artist as well as developing his personal work.

Solo exhibitions include the Truman Brewery, London, 2007, Redchurch Street Gallery, London, 2009, New York Studio Gallery, NYC, 2010, Mercer Street, London, 2011 and Milk Studios, LA, 2013. Baker has also exhibited with the Fine Art Society, collaborated with Sir Paul Smith for a sculpture entitled *Triumph in the Face of Absurdity*, which was displayed at the Victoria and Albert Museum, and continues to be committed to creating work to raise money for many charities. He has recently been commissioned to be a presenter on *The Art Show*. His work is in many international collections.

Although Baker has produced sculptural pieces in a wide and varied choice of materials, as well as many large-scale and detailed drawings, he remains primarily a painter with an interest in narrative and an understanding of the tradition of painting. Known to purposefully damage his work by drilling, cutting and even shooting it, Baker intentionally puts in to question the preciousness of art and the definition of its beauty, adding to the emotive charge of the work he produces. Indeed, Edward Lucie-Smith has described Baker's paintings as having, 'something more, a kind of romantic melancholy that is very British. And sometimes the melancholy turns out to have sharp claws. The pictures make you sit up and examine your conscience.'

Charming Baker lives and works in London.

INNOCENCE
Tales of Youth and Guile

What makes us innocent and how do we come to lose it? Featuring the autobiographical stories telling of Roald Dahl's boyhood and youth as well as four further tales of innocence betrayed, Dahl touches on the joys and horrors of growing up.

Among other stories, you'll read about the wager that destroys a girl's faith in her father, the landlady who has plans for her unsuspecting young guest and the commuter who is horrified to discover that a fellow commuter once bullied him at school.